ERROR AND DECEPTION IN SCIENCE

Essays on biological aspects of life

JEAN ROSTAND

Translated from the French by

A. J. POMERANS

BASIC BOOKS, INC.   NEW YORK

First published in France under the title

SCIENCE FAUSSE ET FAUSSES SCIENCES

English translation © Hutchinson & Co. (Publishers) Ltd. 1960

Published in the United States of America

Basic Books, Inc. 1960

Library of Congress Catalog Card Number: 60-14574

CONTENTS

PREFACE

THIS book, containing a number of essays on apparently unrelated subjects, is held together by a common thread: the desire to plumb the depths of certain biological aspects of life. The title is taken from the first essay which tries to show in what ways scientific knowledge can be perverted by mystifiers and fanatics of every kind and even, unwittingly, by true scientists.

In *Biology and the Law*, I have examined the main legal consequences of recent biological discoveries. These discoveries are likely to play an ever-increasing role in juristic discussions, so much so that forensic biology will one day take its rightful place by the side of forensic medicine.

In *The Singularities of Man*, I have tried to show how nature's own 'experiments' bear on experimental human biology, and in *Biology and Maladjustment*, I have endeavoured to point out the many biological factors that cause abnormal behaviour and how they are related to social and psychological factors of maladjustment. In *Biological Unity and Diversity* I have looked at the differentiating factors that go into the makings of the individual and of the species, and in *Biology, and the Cinema*, I have stressed the important role of the scientific film in our understanding and interpretation of natural phenomena.

I am fully aware that each of the subjects considered merits a much fuller discussion, but I hope that, incomplete though they are, these essays may serve as the starting point for more far-reaching inquiries.

JEAN ROSTAND.

I

Error and Deception in Science

'IN 1593, it was rumoured that a seven-year-old Silesian child, shedding its milk teeth, had grown a gold tooth in place of a molar. Horstius, then Professor of Medicine at the University of Helmstedt, wrote an account of the story and asserted that its causes were partly natural and partly miraculous, and that God had made the child a gift of the golden tooth to console Christendom, so mightily oppressed by the Turks at that time. The consolation and profit that Christianity must have derived from that gift can be imagined! In the same year, lest the tooth lack sufficient historical commentators, Rullandus wrote a further account of it. Two years later, Ingolsteterus, another scholar, published a refutation of Rullandus's theory and Rullandus's elegant and learned reply was not long in coming. Another scholar, Libavius by name, collated all that had been written on the subject and added his own conclusions. Every one of these remarkable works would have been quite perfect in itself, if only the tooth had really been gold. Yet when a goldsmith was finally consulted, it was discovered that the tooth had been skilfully covered with gold leaf. But then, all the learned tomes were written first, and the goldsmith consulted as an afterthought.

'Nothing is easier than to adopt this method in every field. Our ignorance is never so clearly shown up by our inability to explain existing facts, as it is by specious explanations of imaginary phenomena. In other words, not only do we lack principles for arriving at the truth, but we hold others that enable us to commit errors.'

(FONTANELLE: *Histoire des Oracles*.)

No scientist has ever managed to avoid all the pitfalls of his work. Even Pasteur, for all his clear thought and his strict and scrupulous approach, had to retrace his steps on more than one occasion. Scientific errors (which, by the way, may be very fruitful when they are committed by great minds), generally bear the individual stamp of their perpetrators. However, the history of science abounds also with examples of *collective* errors that have given rise to entire schools of false thought. Such large-scale delusions merit our attention if only because they illustrate the power of preconceived ideas: the moment any authority claims to have observed a non-existent phenomenon, many others, though neither his dupes nor deliberate swindlers, are likely to declare that they, too, have seen the same thing.

I believe that of all such infectious illusions there is none to compare with the remarkable story of N-rays. These were 'discovered' by a professor of physics, whose subsequent studies enabled him to list all their properties and even to measure their wave-lengths. Many other scientists repeated his experiments and made striking observations of a phenomenon which, when all is said and done, *never existed* outside their fertile imaginations.

This whole business, so reminiscent of the brain-storms of a psychotic or of a scenario by Jules Romains, happened more than fifty years ago and is now almost forgotten. If we recall it nevertheless, we do so because of its great interest for the scientific historian: the detailed study of the course of a false theory may turn out to be as instructive as that of scientific truth.

At the beginning of 1903, the distinguished physicist, M. René Blondlot – Professor of Science at the University of Nancy, and *Correspondant* of the *Académie des Sciences* – like so many of his colleagues at that time, was devoting his attention to the study of X-rays, discovered a short while earlier by the German physicist Röntgen.

Since X-rays could not then be polarized, Blondlot tried to develop a polarization technique and, in the course of this work he came across new rays that were quite distinct from X-rays and which, unlike the latter, could be polarized.[1]

It is not uncommon for scientists to stumble across facts quite unconnected with their original research: 'Previously I had ascribed polarization to X-rays when, in fact, it was produced by the new rays; this error was unavoidable before the study of refraction effects had been completed. Only after that study did I become convinced that I was not tackling X-rays but an entirely new type of radiation.' (Proceedings of the *Académie des Sciences*, 23 March 1903.)

The new rays had characteristic properties: they could travel through metals and a great many other substances normally opaque to all known spectral radiation.

Blondlot first discovered his rays in the radiation emanating from an X-ray tube, but he soon detected them in many other radiations also, particularly in those emitted by incandescent burners, Nernst filaments, and, more generally, in radiation from ordinary sources of light and heat. He named these new rays 'N-rays' as a tribute to Nancy, the city where they were discovered.

N-radiation was not a simple form of radiation, but a combination of a host of different radiations producing a common effect. In particular, whenever N-rays happened

[13]

to strike a small spark or flame or, for that matter, any luminous object, they increased the brightness of these sources of light. Another of their effects was to increase the phosphorescence of certain chemical compounds, for instance, of calcium sulphide. Of all the N-ray effects – Blondlot noted – increase of phosphorescence was 'the easiest to observe, the experiment being very easily set up and repeated'.

For demonstration purposes, it was said to be helpful to observe the effects of N-rays on reflected light. Whenever a 'pencil' of N-rays was directed at a piece of white paper, the scattered light became appreciably more intense. Needless to say, different individuals observed this 'intensification' in different ways.

'Some people appreciate the increase in the brightness of a small source of light due to N-rays straight away and quite easily, while others find that the increase is hardly perceptible, and only after repeated attempts do they manage to observe it with any certainty. The delicacy of the effects and the extreme care needed in observing these, must not be allowed to stand in the way of studying a phenomenon which has made us familiar with a radiation hitherto unknown.'

Moreover, Blondlot added, by using a powerful Nernst filament (200 watts) – a source particularly rich in N-rays – and by dispensing with the protective glass cylinder, the radiation became so intense that 'to my mind everyone with eyes to see cannot fail to observe it'.

If elementary precautions were taken (avoiding eye-strain, being relaxed, refraining from smoking), 'the observation of N-rays and of allied phenomena can be made by anyone, almost without exception, and I have only encountered three or four people who were unsuccessful'.

Pursuing his methodical inquiry, Blondlot never ceased making further important and significant discoveries. As was to be expected, it was not long before the sun was found to be a source of N-rays, rays of solar origin lending themselves to concentration by quartz lenses. Furthermore, N-rays could be stored by certain substances which, in turn, were capable of re-emitting them as secondary radiation (Proceedings of the *Académie des Sciences*, 9 November 1903). This property of storing and re-emitting N-rays was characteristic of quartz, carbon sulphide, of various types of rock, of fragments of limestone, and of bricks, etc., while aluminium, wood, dry or moist paper, and paraffin, were strictly lacking in it.

Once produced, the secondary radiation was said to continue *for some days*, but only if the surface of the emitting bodies was very dry. This followed from the well-known fact that 'even the thinnest layer of water acts as a barrier to N-rays'.

Then came an altogether unexpected discovery: N-rays not only produced an increase in the brightness of luminous bodies, they also had the direct effect of increasing the intensity of visual sensations. At first this seemed paradoxical: how could N-rays which were arrested by even the thinnest film of water, penetrate into the humours of the eye?

Immediately, the hypothesis suggested itself that, unlike pure water, impure liquids were no barrier to N-rays. Experiment was at once to confirm the validity of the hypothesis; the slightest trace of sodium chloride was enough to render water transparent to N-radiation.

Better still; impure water actually became a store of N-rays!
Here was a unique example of 'phosphorescence in a
liquid body'.

An entirely new field of research had suddenly opened up
to science. And it was not long before sea water was submitted to the test and quite naturally, water so rich in salts,
proved capable of storing and re-emitting the rays in
profusion. Clearly the 'phosphorescence' of sea water had
to play an important role in other fields also. The idea
began to take shape – and it was but a short step from its
inception to its full flowering – that N-rays were not
'without influence on certain factors of animal and vegetable life'. (Proceedings of the *Académie des Sciences*, 28
November 1903.)

Meanwhile, Blondlot had continued his work in the
purely physical realm. He had discovered that external
stresses caused certain substances to emit N-rays: this
happened when a thin strip of glass or a wooden rod was
bent or when a piece of rubber was twisted. With inexorable
logic, Blondlot asked himself if a similar effect was
not also produced whenever any body was in *internal* dis-
equilibrium.

He put this question to the test at once, and experiment
did not keep him waiting long for an affirmative answer:
tempered steel, hard-hammered brass, crystalline sulphur;
all these emitted N-rays spontaneously and continuously.
Needless to say, untempered steel was completely lacking
in radiation potential, while a steel chisel, as it was alter-
nately hardened and softened, proved to be active and
inactive in turn. In the case of tempered steel, the emission
of N-rays appeared to persist indefinitely.

'Turning tools, and branding irons dating from the

seventeenth century, in my family's possession, and certainly never tempered since the time of their making, emit N-rays just as if they had been recently made. A knife recovered from a Graeco-Roman burial ground near Graincourt (Lorraine) which, judging from other objects found in the vicinity (glass and clay vases, fibulae, buckles, a sword of the *sciasamax* type, etc.), dated from Merovingian times, emits N-rays just like a modern knife.'

Now, from the radiation emitted by this ancient weapon, it followed quite clearly that N-rays persisted for more than twelve centuries! Furthermore, as might have been foreseen, it was only the blade and not the handle which proved to be the source of the radiation.

Blondlot was not one to stop half-way. Not content with mere qualitative findings, he set to work to give quantitative meaning to the physical properties of N-rays (reflection, refraction, polarization), and to measure their wavelengths. Using various time-honoured laboratory methods – prisms, lenses, diffraction gratings, and Newton's rings, he performed a host of experiments, and used each set of measurements as a control for all the others. Thus he could proudly claim that 'every wave-length has been determined by three independent series of measurements made with three gratings'.

The results clearly showed good agreement, and Blondlot was entirely satisfied. Even so, he could not hide his surprise that the respective wave-lengths had proved very much shorter than those of visible light. With material of refractive index 1·04, for instance, one method gave a wave-length of 0·0085μ, while another method gave 0·0081μ; with material of refractive index 1·85, the wave-lengths were found to be 0·017μ and

0·0176μ respectively. Who could have asked for better results?

'Although I cannot assess the degree of approximation of the results with any great accuracy, I nevertheless believe that the relative errors are less than 4%.'

February 1904 brought yet another discovery, and one of the greatest importance. At last, successful photographs had been taken not, admittedly, of the N-rays themselves, but of their effects particularly on an electric spark. From then on scientists could study N-ray effects by an irreproachable method (unfortunately it yielded no more than one result in forty attempts), a method which completely eliminated all subjective and personal factors, thus dispelling all the objections of those who, having failed to observe the N-rays themselves, had gone out of their way to put their very existence in doubt.

No wonder that Dr. H. Bordier, lecturer at the Lyons Medical School, took these blind critics to task in the following words:[2] 'Such observers have only themselves to blame; no doubt they used faulty techniques or else the source of radiation was impaired; in any case, the existence of N-rays will never again be put in doubt, particularly now that their action has been recorded *photographically*, i.e. by a purely objective method.'

Almost at the same time, a most delicate experiment was being performed by another scientist, Dr. Th. Guilloz. Guilloz's work not only fascinated Blondlot, but inspired him to put forward a supplementary, very fruitful, idea. If N-rays intensified the brightness of a given source, surely other rays, the so-called inhibitors, must have the opposite effect?

No sooner had this converse effect been postulated, when

its existence was proved experimentally. The 'inhibitors' became known as the N_1-rays, and their investigation was to complement the work on N-rays. This study was undertaken with the same painstaking patience, and the same scientific impartiality that had been the hall-mark of the entire research project.

Blondlot went on to measure the refraction of N_1-rays and to determine their wave-lengths. He discovered that some substances were either exclusive or predominant sources of the new type of radiation. Furthermore, N_1-rays had all the fundamental properties of N-rays; they could be stored by certain substances which re-emitted them by way of secondary radiation and they were emitted by substances under tensional stress. In short, a systematic study showed that N_1-rays were the antithesis of N-rays. Thus N_1-rays reduced the brightness of light emitted normally, but increased that of light emitted tangentially, while N-rays had precisely the opposite effect.

Blondlot was no longer the sole conqueror of the new domain he had opened up – an ever greater number of scientists joined him in his arduous labours. Macé de Lépinay managed to show that sound vibrations gave rise to the emission of N-rays in the vicinity of the antinodes; Guitton detected N-rays in the magnetic field of a bar magnet and of an Hertzian oscillator; Bichat observed them emerging from liquified gases; Charpentier from ozone and aromatic substances; Lambert from soluble ferments; Colson from chemical reactions during the formation of basic salts.

Moreover, Charpentier observed that N-rays were conducted by a copper wire and, more generally, by all substances transparent to them, and Bugard recorded the rotation of their plane of polarization under the influence of a magnet field and also under the influence of certain solutes (aqueous solutions of tartaric acid deflect ordinary light to the right and N-rays to the left). According to Bugard, 'the rotational effect of a sugar solution on a shaft of N-rays of index $1·04$ is 700 times greater than for yellow light'. J. Becquerel declared that anaesthetics (chloroform) decreased the emission of N-rays and, having measured the wave-lengths of different pencils of N- and N_1-rays, he found that they were in simple proportion.

.   .   .   .   .

In December 1903 (Report to the *Académie des Sciences* of 14 December 1903), A. Charpentier and his students opened up an entirely new path in the study of N-radiation. Charpentier was not a man to be ignored – he was Professor of Biophysics at Nancy. His work showed that N-rays, or a very similar type of radiation, played a fundamental role in biology.

Having 'discovered' that these rays were liberated by animals and by man, particularly in the vicinity of muscles and nerves, he rightly attributed to N-rays physiological effects of the greatest importance. Small wonder then that a host of unexpected phenomena was discovered in the space of only a few months. N-rays, or rather the allied 'physiological radiations', were seen to be emitted not only by animal organisms but also by plant tissues – seeds, leaves, roots and bulbs. Though anaesthetics reduced the intensity of the emission, they had a preliminary effect on the rays (excitation phase). As J. Becquerel put it: 'if anaesthetics served no other purpose than to affect the emission of N-rays, they would still be important as evidence that N-radiation constitutes one of the primordial phenomena of vital activity'.

'Physiological radiations' were not due to the storing up of solar N-energy, as the unsuspecting layman might well have believed. Charpentier managed to show that subjects shut away for nine hours in complete darkness showed no decrease in their physiological emissivity.

If the truth be told, physiological radiation was slightly different from N-rays proper: its composition seemed to be somewhat more complex, and while lead and pure water were opaque to N-rays, these substances were partly transparent to physiological radiations. Differences were even observed between the radiation emitted by muscular tissue and that emitted by nervous tissue, the latter being arrested by aluminium, while the former was not.

Thanks to the presence of these 'vital radiations', it became possible – albeit only by very delicate means – to follow the course of a superficial nerve. The rays could be detected not only where the nerve comes close to the surface of the skin, but also – though more weakly – at a distance. This too – Bordier noted – was an important discovery: 'Here we have a new method of investigating muscular and nervous activity; in neurology, particularly, this work has become of very great importance, as no previous method could measure the external reactions of the nervous system.'

Since the spinal cord emitted radiation, its course could be traced *in vivo* by its radiation effects on a phosphorescent calcium sulphide screen; the brightness was most intense in the region of the cervical and lumbar enlargements, these regions being the most intense centres of N-ray emission.

If an experimental subject contracted both his arms, there was an increase in brightness in the region of the cervical enlargement; if he contracted one arm only, the increase in brightness was most noticeable on the corresponding side.

The reader will marvel at the ingenious way in which the experimenters had perfected their techniques!

By similar methods, Charpentier was studying the topography of certain superficial nerve centres, and, in particular, the pre-motor and motor areas of the cerebral cortex. The subject was asked to speak (either loudly, or softly) while a sensitive screen was passed over the left side of his cranium. The screen became brighter as Broca's area (located clinically in a preliminary experiment) was approached. No such effect could be detected when the screen was passed over the right side of the cranium, at least not in the case of normal subjects.

Charpentier went further still: he found a way of detecting pure mental exertion (unaccompanied by any outward signs) from a distance. If a subject merely thought, concentrated, or executed a mental operation (calculation, reasoning), the screen would automatically become brighter. It had become possible to 'demonstrate the mental effort of willing or concentrating not only to an external observer, but even to the subject himself, who could now observe himself thinking'.

André Broca, for his part, studied cerebral radiations by means of a small lead tube bearing a grooved wood plug impregnated with phosphorescent calcium sulphide. If the tube was passed over the cranium, the calcium sulphide changed its brightness, and it was quite obvious that maximum loss of brightness occurred near the cerebral fissures (intercerebral fissure, fissure of Sylvius, fissure of Rolando).

'The experiments are easily repeated and are good practice in N-ray techniques.'

Naturally enough, the intensity of cerebral radiation varied with the intensity of mental activity. Thus, in the case of dogs anaesthetized by ether (or by any other anaesthetic), J. Becqueral and A. Broca found an initial emission of N-rays in *enormous quantities*. However, as the dog went under more completely, the emission diminished, until finally the N-rays gave way completely to N_1-rays.

Similarly, if respiration was increased by nervous excitation, a suitable screen applied near the medullary respiratory centre registered an intense emission of N-rays, while impeded respiration gave rise to the emission of N_1-rays.

The physiological effects of N-rays were legion: they enhanced not only our visual acuity, but also the sensitivity of the retina (J. Becquerel), and our sense of smell (Charpentier), hearing and taste. Their effect on the visuo-sensory area of the cortex was demonstrated by passing a source of radiation (a blade of tempered steel, for instance) over the left side of the cranium, when an increase in the brightness of the external object could be observed over most of the posterior parietal lobe and the neighbouring occipital lobe. According to the discoverer of this method (Charpentier), the maximum effect was produced when the object was held some four centimetres above the occipital lobe. This position corresponded to the visuo-sensory area.

Moreover, N-rays could be made to act on the medullary centres. If a small source of N-rays were placed above the seventh cervical vertebra, a dilatation of the pupils from 0·5 to 1 millimetre, and sometimes more, was produced, depending only on the sensitivity of the subject and the intensity of the source (Charpentier and E. Meyer).

According to Charpentier, N-rays (and their effects) could be propagated along the nerves from any point of the body. 'If a small, slightly insulated, calcium sulphide screen is held in, or placed on the tips of, the fingers, until it has reached a state of luminous equilibrium, its brightness will increase slightly when any point on the hand, the arm or any other part of the skin is touched by a source of N-rays.' By moving such a source over the cranium, Charpentier managed to locate a definite point of maximum brightness: 'the point seems to be that level of the Rolandic area known to correspond to the fingers holding the screen'.

'The excitation of these areas can, it is true, be produced by means of a Farradic current also, but how much more elegant, and above all, how much less tiring for the subject, is excitation by imperceptible N-rays' (Bordier).

Who could fail to appreciate the tremendous importance and the incomparable value of this new method, which made possible the complete anatomical investigation of the nervous paths of living subjects? Nor must we forget the therapeutic and diagnostic applications of this new-found knowledge. A host of diseases could now be diagnosed by means of characteristic changes in the intensity of the emitted radiation.

We are indebted to A. Broca and Zimmern for a whole series of observations concerning the effects of age or of illness on the spinal emissive centres. These centres are fixed and of clearly defined activity, the most active points corresponding to the second, fifth and eleventh dorsal vertebrae, to the second lumbar vertebra and to the middle of the sacrum. The second dorsal maximum probably corresponds to the cilio-spinal centre; that of the second lumbar to the genital, vesical and defecation centres. The emissive centres, and particularly those corresponding to the second lumbar vertebra are less pronounced in elderly people.

Hysterectomies give rise to marked differences in radiation, depending on whether the ovaries have been removed or not. A full bladder may increase the intensity of the radiation, or so it would appear from an observation by Broca and Zimmern.

In the course of a 'clinical' examination, when the emission of N-rays was recorded on a screen, Broca found that a woman whose ovaries had been removed long before, showed hardly any second lumbar radiation; this was only to be expected. But a little later, his collaborator, Zimmern, discovered to his surprise that he could clearly discern signs of greater radiation. Was this merely a difference in sensitivity on the part of the two observers? Not at all. The explanation was quite simple: during the second examination, the subject had experienced an urgent need to urinate, with a consequent stimulation of radiation pressure. The patient having relieved herself, a third examination produced complete agreement between the two physicians, both of whom could now diagnose the absence of all radiation in that region.

Other workers described changes in N-radiation due to various diseases affecting the nervous or muscular system: paralysis, neuritis, poliomyelitis, and so on.

On 22 February 1904, Drs. Gilbert Ballet and Delherm

presented a paper to the *Académie des Sciences* on a case of primary myopathy; while the facial emission of N-rays had remained normal, there was a decrease of radiation from the level of the digital extensors and a further decrease from the level of the deltoid; these differences clearly reflected the differences in muscular tonus: unimpaired facial muscles, complete atrophy of the deltoid, and partial atrophy of the muscles of the forearm.

In a case of right-sided paralysis (hemiplegia) dating from the patient's childhood, Dr. Fabre noticed that the N-rays were being emitted from the right temple, the centre of speech (centre of Broca) normally situated in the left hemisphere of the brain, having been supplanted by a centre in the right hemisphere.

Fabre also reported the emission of N-rays through contractions of the uterus during labour, the intensity of the emission being proportional to the force of the contractions.[3]

Finally, Charpentier and Meyer, by performing experiments on living dogs, discovered a most curious fact that promised to have far-reaching clinical applications: when the appropriate screen was impregnated with certain chemical substances, notably with alkaloids, the effect on that screen of physiological radiation was greatly increased. Moreover, the increases were *selective* since they occurred exclusively in the case of organs affected by the particular substance: digitalis – which affects the action of the heart – increased the intensity of cardiac radiation, while pilocarpine which stimulates glandular secretion, increased the intensity of glandular radiation. Similarly, chloral increased cerebral radiation, thyroid extract increased thyroid radiation, testosterone increased testicular radiation.

Physicians were now in a position to use a whole battery of screens of differential sensitivity, each suited to the investigation of a particular organ.

.　　　.　　　.　　　.　　　.

This, in brief, was the high degree of perfection that research on N-radiation and physiological radiation had attained by 1904, less than two years after its inception. Here was an imposing edifice of positive facts with far-reaching effects not only in physics, biology and medicine, but in all the theoretical and applied sciences.

What a pity then, that this whole edifice had to come tumbling down only a few months later. It was not simply a case of reinterpreting or discarding some of the assumptions. The whole of Blondlot's framework was thrown out, hook, line and sinker.

Doubting voices had been raised from the very beginning of Blondlot's discovery and some specialist objections had never been silenced effectively. Still, no amount of doubting or criticism had been able to halt the triumphant progress of the new science. All the world had clearly observed a phenomenon that had never existed. Then, almost overnight, the hypnotic spell was broken.

The Nancy group and some of its faithful managed to put up some slight resistance, but the whole business was dropped and buried once and for all. N-rays, N_1-rays, and physiological radiations would never again grace the pages of scientific journals, in which they had cut so marvellous a figure.

The reader must forgive us if we have detained him so long with so full an account of a mere error. Needless to say, it was not our intention to go out of our way to malign those scientists who fell victim to this delusion; rather did we feel that there is much food for thought in this sad business.

The most astonishing facet of the episode is the extraordinarily great number of people who were taken in. These people were not pseudo-scientists, charlatans, dreamers, or mystifiers; far from it, they were true men of science, disinterested, honourable, used to laboratory procedure, people with level heads and sound common sense. This is borne out by their subsequent achievements as Professors, Consultants and Lecturers. Jean Becquerel, Gilbert Ballet, André Broca, Zimmern, Bordier – all of them have made their contribution to science.

No less extraordinary is the *degree of consistency, and of apparent logic that pervaded the whole of this collective delusion*; all the results were consistent, and agreed within fairly narrow limits.[4] Who can deny Blondlot's great feat in arriving at compatible values of the wave-lengths of these non-existent rays by several distinct methods!

Lucien Cuénot has suggested[5] that the whole discovery of N-rays might well have been initiated by an over-zealous laboratory assistant who tried to make himself indispensable to the worthy Nancy professor.

In the same paper, Cuénot goes on to say: 'All critics (and all investigators have to be their own critics first and foremost) must be sceptical of everything – of their desire to make new discoveries and above all of their right-hand men: assistants are not usually given to a scrupulous love of truth, and have little aversion to rigging experiments;

they are quite ready to flatter their superiors by presenting them with results that agree with their *a priori* notions. Alternatively, they often get malicious pleasure out of deceiving their superiors, thus driving them to commit errors – envy and ingratitude often go hand in hand. Scientists must also be suspicious of their own relatives – family ties are no safeguards against deception; on the contrary, it is often thought great fun to make a fool of a great man: there are known cases of children deliberately misleading their fathers, or fathers-in-law.'

While we have no evidence that flattery or deception was at the roots of the discovery of N-rays, we may take it that the urge to make new discoveries, so powerful in all men of science, played a considerable role from the very start. Coupled with this urge were *preconceived ideas, and auto-suggestion* together with the desire to break new ground.

The remarkable history of N-rays is full of morals both for the individual, and also for the social, psychologist. No doubt it would have delighted the author of the *Histoire des Oracles.*

.   .   .   .   .

If highly trained scientists could fall victim to these mass delusions, it need not surprise us to learn that delusion holds an even greater sway among pseudo-scientists.

A love of miracles and mystery, of magic and the super-natural, together with rank mythomania and self-seeking charlatanism are here combined with incredible gullibility. While science quickly rectifies its errors (the whole N-ray business lasted for only two years) the pseudo-sciences can persist in their delusions without let or hindrance.

Pseudo-sciences are important factors in our social life. If we were to take stock of the followers of radiesthesia, of astrology, of metapsychics, etc., we should discover that they far outnumber the more earth-bound scientists. Nor do these mystifiers need to expend a great deal of their energy on propaganda – their armies require little encouragement.

In France, and, I fear, in the rest of the world also, radiesthesia takes first place among these pseudo-scientific delusions. Its roots lie far back in history, but radiesthesia only came into its own in 1927, when it was given its present name by the Abbé Bouly. According to its disciples, 70 to 80 per cent of our fellow men possess a special faculty, a sixth sense as it were, which enables them to discover such things as subterranean sources of water or oil, deposits of ore, human remains, and so on.

Radiesthesia is practised by means of an 'amplifying instrument' – a ring or a pendulum – which is set into motion by a muscular reflex due to the unconscious perception of the presence of the desired object. The 'experts' are divided in their interpretation of this strange gift of divination, some giving an occult and others a 'physical' explanation. According to the latter, the object itself emits some form of radiation which those with the special faculty can 'receive', while the former believe that, like telepathy or clairvoyance, the special gift is one of second sight.

Some of these experts are particularly adept at diagnosing the sex of a foetus by holding a pendulum above the mother's abdomen. Most use their 'gift' for medical diagnosis, detecting visceral lesions, states of latent morbidity, parasitic infestations, etc.

This type of *medical radiesthesia* is very popular, indeed, particularly since it can *diagnose diseases at a distance*, using no more than a drop of blood, of urine or of saliva, or else a hair, a photograph or even a simple piece of paper on which the patient has placed his hands. These objects simply increase the mental concentration of the diagnostician.

One such practitioner, working with no more than a single hair, is said to have taken the blood pressure of a patient thousands of miles away (the 'practitioner' was in France, the patient on the island of Mauritius in the Indian Ocean!). Similar 'teleradiesthesic' procedures are used for locating springs or mines, the expert working on maps or on regional charts.

Radiesthesia exists in many different forms. Thus, followers of the 'Turenne method' measure a patient's 'wave-length', with a special rod which is eight metres long when used to measure a normal subject and shorter in cases of illness or organic deficiency. Other experts use a pack of playing cards bearing medical information. The pack is shuffled and cut and dealt out on the table, and a pendulum is consulted in the presence of either the patient or of his representative. When the pendulum points to a particular card, all that remains is to read off the diagnosis.

But radiesthesia does more than merely diagnose diseases, it also prescribes the appropriate therapy. When a pendulum is left to swing over an assortment of vials containing various medicaments, it will infallibly come to rest over the required cure. Moreover, cures can be effected from a distance. This is done by setting off 'favourable waves' which break up bacteria, or else help to increase the wave-lengths of the affected organs.

Nor does the usefulness of radiesthesia stop there. Radiesthesia is found quite invaluable by fishermen, hunters, pharmacists, geologists, archaeologists, physiologists, astronomers. . . . 'The surface of a planet can be studied on paper, simply by drawing a circle of any radius and by marking any point of its circumference with the symbol of the planet which can be found in any almanac. All that remains is to work with the required indicators: water, various rocks, snow, ice, etc.'[6] A similar method can also be used for investigating the interior of the planets, the stars and the comets; for discovering unknown regions; for proving that the moon is hollow, that Jupiter has a large island surrounded by an almost circular ocean, that the stars have pits full of heavy water, that Wegener's theory (on the origin of continents) is questionable, etc.

Military strategists have a lot to learn from radiesthesia and it is invaluable to the police in bringing criminals or escaped prisoners to heel, or in detecting fraudulent practices. Radiesthesia is also invaluable in private life (choosing a job, a partner, a husband or wife). Since perfect wedlock depends on the union of positive and negative, it is essential to determine the polarity of the two prospective partners. As luck would have it, the polarity can be ascertained from a distance. Strict measurements of the wave-lengths of the genital organs, make it possible to prognosticate sexual compatibility (Liliane Jauzin).

Need we stress that this whole business is nothing but utter folly, and that whenever any of these 'experts' has been put to a strict and controlled test, his successes were never greater than simple probability calculation might have led one to suspect.[7] Needless to say, some of these experts have committed the most appalling blunders, as when they diagnosed pregnancy in a fireman, or a tumour of the prostate in a nun.

For anyone with the slightest training in science, there can be no doubt that *the problems posed by radiesthesia simply do not exist*, the only puzzle being how so many people of normal intelligence can be taken in by this form of systemized insanity.

'What is so extraordinary is that radiestheisa numbers among its followers so many people who ought to know better' (Cuénot, in a personal letter).[8]

Radiesthesists range from innocent believers to crude impostors and charlatans (whose presence is admitted by even the faithful). It is easy to persuade oneself of the efficacy of so financially rewarding a message and, in any case, it is certainly less trouble to buy a pendulum than to study pathology.[9]

'Radiesthesia in nine lessons,' promises Col. Le Gall, a former student at the *École Polytechnique* and a former lecturer in applied science at the *École d'artillerie* in Fontainebleau. 'To use the pendulum,' another 'doctor of radiesthesia', M. Henry de France, writes, 'all that is needed is a slight exertion of the intellect and a minimum of manual dexterity in holding the ring or pendulum correctly.'

Alas, radiesthesia is still flourishing in the land. Queues still form outside the consulting rooms of its medical 'practitioners'. There are associations of medical radiesthesists, societies for research into radiesthesia, radiesthesia universities, advanced courses in radiesthesia, correspondence courses in radiesthesia, libraries, pamphlets and special reviews (not to mention the free publicity of the popular magazines). There are special shops for selling the various paraphernalia used in radiesthesia: whalebone rings, black ebony Mermet pendulums, plastic Lesourd pendulums, ivory-tipped pendulums for work on maps or on anatomical charts (500 francs), Le Gall bimetallic pendulums (costing as much as 880 francs including balls and chain) and high-grade pendulums for mineral divining (3,500 francs), specially sensitized pendulums made of semi-precious stones – agate, chalcedony, sunstone (2,000 francs). Nor can any of these prices be guaranteed; they are subject to fluctuation and were taken from a French catalogue dated 1950.

As for the public, who would be surprised at its incredible gullibility? The man in the street lacks the training to see through all the verbiage of people who give themselves scientific airs and who use so impressive a vocabulary.[10]

It is only fair to add that these 'practitioners' – just like other 'healers' – do in fact produce cures for certain psycho-somatic complaints, simply by suggestion. No doubt, the more the patient is struck by the magic enchantment of the techniques, the more effective the cure becomes. At this point, the reader might well object that, this being the case, such 'practitioners' may be said to play some useful part and should, therefore, best be left alone.

This raises the quite extraneous problem of how a rational person ought to behave when faced with utterly irrational behaviour which, precisely because of its irrationality, has some effects on man's *irrational* attitudes. In the case of these 'healers', moreover, it must always be borne in mind that while they may produce 'cures', they can also have the detrimental effect of dissuading people,

[34]

desperately in need of medical attention, from consulting a qualified physician.

.　　　.　　　.　　　.　　　.

While we may say that no reputable scientist has ever taken radiesthesia seriously, the same is not true of metapsychics. Thus Freud and Carrel believed in telepathy, and Crookes, Oliver Lodge, Crawford and Richet in telekinesis, i.e. the materialization of psychic forces. At this very moment, serious scientists look with some favour on the experimental work of Rhine, who claims to have shown, by strict statistical methods, the existence of extra-sensory perception and the effect of mind over matter.[11]

'Experiments such as those of Rhine and Tyrell on extra-sensory guessing, experiences such as those of Gilbert Murray on thought transference, and the numerous sporadic records of telepathy and clairvoyance suggest that some people at least possess possibilities of knowledge which are not confined within the ordinary channels of sense perception' (Julian Huxley: *The Uniqueness of Man*, Chatto & Windus, 1941, p. 30).

I, personally, am convinced that there is not an ounce of truth in any of these notions.

Until I am proved wrong, I shall continue to take all *psychic* phenomena (occult movement of objects, levitation, materialization, etc.) for crude superstition. As regards the so-called *mental* phenomena (telepathy, premonitions, clairvoyance, etc.) I think that some must be attributed to pure coincidence and others to unconscious or – far more frequently – to deliberate deception.

In my own youth, I performed a great number of

[35]

experiments with 'mediums', both at the *Institut meta-psychique* and also elsewhere. In the course of this work, which was fairly comprehensive while it lasted, I came to the conclusion that under even half-way satisfactory conditions it is quite impossible to observe any kind of 'supernormal' phenomenon whatsoever. Moreover, I have found that all believers in metapsychics have so unscientific a mental attitude that they seem hall-marked by nature for creating and entertaining every possible kind of illusion.

Metapsychics beliefs usually fulfil strong emotional needs, and give a great deal of psychological relief in that they either satisfy an innate propensity for magic, or else confirm the existence of life in the hereafter. In any case, belief in metapsychics is almost invariably the result of so strong a 'need to believe', that the critical faculties are completely deadened.

If, time after time, a medium fails to bring convincing proof of her prowess, we are told: 'Surely you cannot expect her to perform to order' or else: 'It's your own obstinacy and your own scepticism which are at fault – a medium, just like a hypersensitive mechanism, is thrown out of gear by the slightest jolt. The medium can only function successfully in an atmosphere of sympathy and trust; when faith is lacking, the medium cannot produce results. . . .'

If we object to darkness, we may be told that, just as a photographic plate cannot be developed in bright light, so a medium might only function when the lights are dimmed. If we ask for the light to be switched on in the middle of a seance, to see if the medium has moved from her place, we shall be told that this is the last thing we must do. The medium might die of shock.

And if we should happen to catch the medium out, so that

she herself has to admit the deception, we are sure to be told that this particular fraud cannot be blamed on metapsychics as a whole. Nor does it entitle us to doubt the medium's own past or future results. The medium may have been out of contact with the higher forces at this particular time, and, in order not to disappoint us, she may have simulated effects which, normally, she would have had no difficulty in producing in the right way. And so on. . . .

In view of the foregoing, the reader might find it extremely difficult to explain why a number of leading scientists should accept the 'findings' of metapsychics. Actually, their support carries little weight, for, when it comes to unfamiliar fields, scientists are often completely uncritical. Incapable of deception themselves, and used to observing nature, which never deceives, they are hard put to it to suspect others of fraud.

Furthermore, scientists are often carried away by their own highly developed imaginations. This is what Arago had to say of Ampère (and his remarks apply with equal force to other scientists).

'Ampère's gullibility has become almost proverbial, though that gullibility was the direct result of his own rich imagination and genius. On hearing of any unusual experiment, after his initial astonishment, he would quickly bring his sharp and fertile mind to bear on the problem, and, seizing on possibilities that would have confused people of lesser intelligence, he would leave no stone unturned until, somehow, he had managed to fit the experiment into the framework of science.'

While Arago himself suspected all forms of clairvoyance (seeing through walls or other opaque bodies), he felt that he would be lacking in his scientific duty if he refused to take part in séances where such phenomena were allegedly demonstrated, provided only that he was allowed to safeguard himself against being tricked.

Though Arago's approach showed a great deal of laudable impartiality, this type of attitude is a godsend to all swindlers. Henri Poincaré was much wiser when he said that he was quite incapable of judging the validity of experiments in metapsychics.

'One has to be on the alert all the time and keep all one's wits about one. Being incapable of doing this, I should certainly be an easy dupe. These experiments would only serve some purpose if they were performed in the presence of an illusionist, a man, who unlike myself, is trained to spot any sleight of hand, and if, furthermore, they were performed in broad daylight and before a camera.' (Quoted by Marcel Boll.)

If metapsychics revels in the support some leading scientists have given it – and these scientists are constantly upheld as shining examples of broadmindedness and intellectual freedom – it is only the better to deride the pigheadedness of orthodox science which, on the whole, has so far refused to be taken in by these strange phenomena. Orthodox scientists are reproached for rejecting the findings of metapsychics out of hand. This reproach is completely unjustified, since many – to my mind, far too many – have turned their backs on metapsychics only after careful and unprejudiced investigations.

As Cuénot put it so well: 'The "non-orthodox" never realize how much the "orthodox" are on the look-out for any new facts, and with how much zeal and enthusiasm they throw themselves into the study of unusual phenomena.

[38]

The greater the jolt to their previous theories, the greater their interest in the new findings.'

No one can deny that orthodox science, too, has committed grave mistakes, and that it has often been guilty of rejecting truths when it ought to have welcomed them. No wonder that the quacks proclaim these classical blunders from the house-tops: the refusal by the *Académie des Sciences* to accept the existence of fossil man and of meteorites, or the refusal by the *Académie de Médecine* to accept Pasteur's work.

We must therefore admit that credibility is a very relative term, and that disbelief may well result from exaggerated faith in established knowledge. Let us also admit quite frankly that the outright rejection of metapsychics – like all outright rejections – carries a measure of intellectual risk.

For my part, I have no hesitation in running this risk, since, from personal experience, I have every reason to believe that, to all intents and purposes, it is altogether negligible.

.   .   .   .   .

If we are ever to put a stop to metapsychical delusions, or to pseudo-scientific delusions in general, it will be less by a frontal attack than by re-education, and *preventive mental hygiene*. Our young must be imbued with a critical spirit immunized against the written or printed lie, and provided with intellectual foundations on which gullibility cannot prosper. We must teach them the meaning of coincidence, probability, admissible conclusions, logical inference, warn them against unconscious resistance to the truth, explain to them the value of fact and experimental proof and, above all, put them on their guard against accepting hearsay evidence. This is best done if they could be made to memorize the story of the 'golden tooth' and if they were enjoined to ponder over the sad history of N-rays.

I remember that in my own adolescence, I read the metapsychical works of Albert de Rochas with keen interest. In his *Extériorisation de la sensibilité*, de Rochas described experiments in which a 'sensitive' subject distinguished the poles of an electro-magnet by its distinct polar 'emanations', the North Pole having a blue and the South Pole a red aura. Now, young as I then was, I could not *possibly* have realized that the whole business – reported with so much 'scientific objectivity' – was utter nonsense from beginning to end. Similarly, whenever I was told about some 'super-normal' phenomenon, I was in no position to reject the evidence out of hand.

Since then I have become a self-made sceptic, and have slowly come to appreciate the fact that many a book consists of nothing but lies, that entire libraries are devoted to the works of impostors, and that the most intelligent and best-informed of men do not always talk the least nonsense or make the least mistakes. I have learned that no fact is ever reported just as it happened, since however truthful and disinterested he may be, every witness is prone to unconscious fabrication. Above all, I have learned to suspect those very slight and unconscious modifications which can so twist a 'fact' that it becomes something quite different.

If only this valuable acquisition, scepticism, could be handed to others on a platter! Alas, each one of us has to acquire it for himself, and to bear the taunts of those who will for ever accuse him of being a doubting Thomas.

* * * * *

The third scientific delusion we shall discuss is the story of Michurin 'biology', a perfect example of the pitfalls of ideological dogmatism. First we looked at the scientists, then at the witch-doctors, and now we shall catch a glimpse of the fanatics.

In France, the whole sad business started in 1948, when the poet Louis Aragon launched a bombshell in the journal *Europe*. Aragon had appointed himself the champion of a new biology, recently adopted by the Central Committee of the Communist Party of the U.S.S.R.

'In no other country,' Aragon wrote fervently, 'and at no other time has so much publicity been given to a scientific discussion. . . . For the first time in history, the work of an entire people is bound up with scientific research.'

From 1948 to 1952, Michurin biology was in full and noisy swing. All notions of classical genetics were rejected, Western biology was put on trial, Mendelian inheritance was dismissed as the ravings of a monk, and mutation was said to be too accidental to matter. The existence of genes and the continuity of chromosomes was denied, and hence the entire chromosome theory. Fertilization by the single sperm was decried as a *bourgeois* misconception, since the greater the number of spermatozoa uniting with one ovum, the more vigorous the result. It was given out that graft hybrids were clear evidence for the inheritance of acquired characters, that changes in the environment produced changes in the heredity of an organism and thus led to sudden variations, so much so that one species could become transformed into another under our very eyes. Thus rye could engender wheat, weeds could produce useful plants, and vegetable cells could be formed out of crystals, etc.

The better to illustrate the nature of this incredible

twentieth-century *scientific delirium*, we add the following quotations:

'Our Michurin biology has proved beyond doubt that vegetable species can be engendered by other vegetable species. In other words, Michurin biology has shown that plants belonging to one species are engendered not only by other plants of the same species, for instance rye by rye, barley by barley, etc., but, under suitable conditions, by other species as well. Today we have a great deal of evidence to show that rye can be engendered by wheat, and what is more, by different species of wheat. These species of wheat can also engender barley, just as rye can engender wheat. Oats can engender wild oats. Everything depends on the conditions under which these plants develop.' (Lysenko, 1950, *Questions scientifiques, Biologie*, La Nouvelle Revue critique, 1953.) What an amazing return to the crude transformist ideas that held sway before Ray and Linaeus!

And now for a return to pre-Pasteurian ideas:

'Cells,' Mme O. Lepechinskaya writes, 'multiply not only by division but also by decomposition into minute granules which develop in turn to give rise to new cells with new properties.

'In my studies of aloe juice,' this biologist added, 'I have found that the crystals, which form in the juice on addition of nucleic acid, give rise to cells.' (*Questions scientifiques*, 1953.)

And the bacteriologist Bochian proclaimed the spontaneous generation of viruses and bacteria.

All these theories were 'proved' by experiments whose puerility takes us back two or three centuries. In the Proceedings of their Academy of Science, we can read that rabbits can transmit tick-bite marks to their descendants, that chickens change their strain when another strain's 'white' is introduced into their egg, that 'giant cows' with monstrous udders have been bred, that fantastic hybrids have been produced, and that chicks fathered by several cocks have been hatched out, etc.

All these fabrications went hand in hand with crude accusations against anyone who refused to accept the 'evidence'. Such people were decried as idealists, meta-physicists, *bourgeois* obscurantists, falsifiers and perverters of science, representatives of a lying, ridiculous, scholastic, impotent biology.

How deplorable an era in which science, debased and stupefied by politics, serves as a pretext for an ugly polemic whose abusive and impassioned exhortations belong to the market-place and not to the intellectual arena! We have no desire to go into the root causes of this great fallacy: ideological prejudice, Stalin's personal influence, plain ignorance or fear of being out of step.[12]

What does concern us, however, is the fact that, the moment Michurinism was proclaimed official dogma in the U.S.S.R., the vast majority of communists throughout the world, accepted this scientific monstrosity as gospel truth.[13]

In France some party biologists kept silent, some were so naïve as to believe the whole business, and some who knew better, took the official line for the sake of the cause. No doubt they felt it was their 'duty' to put party discipline before respect for scientific truth. Still, I am no expert on the more delicate aspects of partisan morality.

As for the ordinary party member who could not be expected to be conversant with the scientific principles at stake or with the real problems involved, who could blame him if he followed blindly where those who ought to have known better led the way? Moreover, the new dogma was seductive by its very audacity, so strikingly different from the prudence of orthodox biology. How easy to mistake this dashing approach for revolutionary thought! How tempting to believe that only because it was befogged by class prejudice did '*bourgeois*' science oppose the great revelations of 'proletarian science'!

Every man jack of them now held clear-cut opinions about the transmission of acquired characters, the mechanisms of heredity, organic evolution, the origin of cells. Those who did not agree, were capitalist lickspittles and enemies of the working class. Whoever was not for Michurin, whoever failed to believe in Lysenko's tomatoes or Lepechinskaya's granules, betrayed the people by his very lack of faith. He was simply a supporter of social iniquity, a 'political aggressor'. . . . Parliamentarians, journalists and laboratory workers – all joined in the public expression of enthusiasm for Michurin.

The following tirade is taken from an article by Georges Cogniot, in *L'Humanité*:[14]

'These are great days for biology – the dawn of the new biology which will change living nature. . . .

'One need surely be no scientist to realize that two diametrically opposed tendencies have crystallized in biology: the progressive materialist tendency based on the Soviet naturalist Michurin, and the idealist and mystical tendency founded by the reactionary biologists Weismann, Mendel and Morgan. . . . A decisive blow has been struck at the theory of mutation, a theory which is the enemy of all rational thought. . . ."

Pointing out that it is no accident that this astounding victory over nature took place 'in the country of the practical rebuilders of the world', Cogniot continued: 'The progressive workers of all nations will rejoice over this additional confirmation of the truth of dialectical materialism. They will rejoice over this new defeat of reactionary ideas, hostile to their emancipation. . . . The glory of Marxist thought is enhanced even further. Marxist education has found a new weapon in combating the capitalist assault on man's conscience. . . .'

And Molotov saluted the triumph of 'true science based on materialist principles, over reactionary and outworn idealist concepts in scientific research'. (Address to the Special Session of the Moscow Soviet, 6 November 1948.)

'What are we to conclude?' Waldeck-Rochet added his voice. 'Quite simply, that metaphysics and philosophical idealism act as brakes on the development of science, while dialectical materialism is a powerful instrument for its advancement.'

And Robert Boundry, in *Europe* (June 1952): 'We can see a clear difference in objective which goes far beyond the field of science. We have, in fact, two opposed philosophical and social conceptions.'

And Robert Cohen: 'The victory of Michurinism has put biology on its feet. . . . The whole of Russia is behind Lysenko. . . .'

And equally certain of proclaiming the truth, Jeanne Levy of the Paris Medical School, wrote: 'Their thesis (i.e. the thesis of Michurin biologists) springs from the very principles of dialectical materialism, the most powerful tool in scientific thought.'

.   .   .   .   .

What has remained of all these dogmatic effusions

today? Nothing, whatsoever. 'Michurin biology' foundered pitifully, and its two heroes, Lysenko and Olga Lepechinskaya, were dismissed as common demagogues.

In a recent issue of *La Pensée*, M. Marcel Prenant explained it all as follows: 'The disappearance of Stalin, and the Twentieth Congress of the Communist Party of the U.S.S.R., have set a new course. . . . The idea of the absolute and formal opposition between bourgeois and proletarian science has been dropped, and only the indisputable idea of different trends of scientific work under different economic systems has been retained. Hand in hand with this change, went the relegation, almost to the point of complete oblivion, of people like T. D. Lysenko and Ogla Lepechinskaya, around whom, a complete mythology had been built up over the years.'

In the same article, Prenant mentions the many grave mistakes, 'committed by Lysenko's supporters against the scientific method'. He admits that 'Lysenko's biology foundered because of its theoretical weakness', that 'talk of "intervarietal wheat" can no longer be heard', that 'the giant Kostroma cow failed to bear giant calves' and that 'its creator, Shaumyan, was dismissed long ago for handing in reports that were far removed from the truth', and that 'the decision taken by the Twentieth Congress to cultivate American maize hybrids, is based on the acceptance of the Mendelian theory of heterosis and is therefore an official disavowal of Lysenko and his methods'.

And, with unimpeachable logic, this Marxist biologist concludes that a science is soon abandoned 'if it substitutes summary approximations and hollow formulae without valid experimental evidence for the serious and conscientious study of the facts'.

[46]

Similar opinions are expressed by Massimo Aloisi (*La Situation dans les sciences biologiques*), who reproaches Olga Lepechinskaya – and elsewhere Lysenko – for having fallen victim to a vitalist(!) error, and for having adopted a 'completely absurd' position. As for Bochian and his spontaneous origin of viruses and bacteria, Aloisi thinks they are not even worth criticizing.

The only defender of Michurin biology left today is M. Roger Garaudy:[15] 'The alleged disgrace of Michurin biology in the Soviet Union, is nothing but a falsification for political ends. Last year's publication in the U.S.S.R. of a Textbook of Dialectical Materialism absolutely disproved that allegation. One has but to read this book to appreciate that every single law of dialectics and every single principle of materialism has been illustrated with examples taken from the works of Michurin and his followers. . . . On page 116 the theories of Mendel, Weismann and Morgan are cited as examples of metaphysical theories, which, under the deceptive cloak of neo-Darwinism, lead to a denial of evolution and to theories of preformation. . . .'[16]

M. Garaudy notwithstanding, there is no doubt that the great days of Michurin biology which provided so many sensational headlines for communist papers and journals – the creation of life, the creation of new species, the collapse of Mendelo-Morganian genetics – have passed. There remain, and that only on the most charitable of views, some doubtful facts and vague interpretations which orthodox genetics cannot as yet explain but which, once they are understood more fully, may be fitted into the general framework and which, in any case, gave no reason whatever for the song and dance Michurin biologists made about them.

Need we stress that the more recent experiments of Benoit and his collaborators (on directed mutations in ducks under the action of D.N.A.; see p. 81) are no corroboration of Michurin biology? Those who used these experiments as evidence for the heredity of acquired traits and for claiming that they spelt the death of Morganian theory, simply showed that they had no idea what these experiments were about.

. . . . .

If we have thought fit to recall this sad adventure, and if we have dwelt at length on the rise and fall of Michurin biology, it was not to prove how right we have been all along,[17] nor for that matter to attack – under a scientific cloak – an idea of society which we believe to be eminently respectable and which we should be willing to support if only it did not go hand in hand with the most absurd and retrograde intellectual obscurantism. We have discussed Michurin biology, simply because it drives home an important lesson.

We simply cannot shrug off the whole affair with: 'Well, anyone can make a mistake in science, and Michurin biology was just another of those scientific errors of which so many have been committed, particularly in biology. No, Michurin biology was *not* just an ordinary error. It was a delusion *based on ideological indoctrination.*

We have seen what importance and what philosophic weight yesterday's Marxists attached to this doctrine. If we imagine how they would have rejoiced in victory, we shall be chary of forgetting the unforgivable scientific, historic and philosophic lies they proffered all along this controversy.

Of course, we must not pay them back in their own coin. We must never claim that *bourgeois* science has triumphed over proletarian science, that only the idealist approach in biology is fruitful, that reactionary and metaphysical philosophy is superior to materialism. We must simply and firmly declare – and it is our right and duty to do so – that *all ideologies* are bad counsellors for the scientist, that no scientist can set his course by the Marxist compass (a compass that is either faulty, or else too delicate to manipulate), and that Claude Bernard is right to this day when he claimed that all doctrinal dictatorships *whatsoever* are just so many impediments to the search for the truth.

REFERENCES

[1] Cf. *Actualités scientifiques:* N-rays. Summary of the papers presented to the Académie des Sciences by R. Blondlot, Gauthiers-Villars, 1904.

[2] N-rays and N_1-rays. *Actualités médicales*, Baillière, 1905.

[3] Note to the *Société médicale des Hopitaux de Lyon*, 23 February 1904.

[4] Unlike X-rays, N-rays were not discovered all at once: it was thanks to his methodical research directed at quite a different aim, that M. Blondlot had the honour of discovering the new radiations. This wonderful discovery is a remarkable example of the power of the scientific method when it goes hand in hand with induction and experiment' (Bordier).

[5] Science and Pseudo-Sciences. *Revue Scientifique*, January 1940.

[6] *See* 'Geology and Radiesthesia', by Lt.-Col. Albert de Blois, *Initiation et Science*, July-September 1956.

[7] When their results fell short of probability the experts claimed triumphantly that this 'negative discrepancy' was just as eloquent

a proof of their powers as a positive discrepancy would have been.

[8] *See also*, Cuénot: *Revue scientifique*, 1 January 1940, *and also* A. Lumière: 'La Crestomancie ou devination par le pendule', *La Revue des Deux Mondes*, 1 April 1948.

[9] The reader may recall Kant's pronouncement on the role of ignorance in superstitions: 'It is no easy matter to acquire the wisdom and learning of the natural philosopher; what better way then of disguising this shortcoming than to put out theories about things that cannot be seen or understood by anyone, and which can consequently be judged in any way whatever without an adversary being able to gainsay one.'

[10] I take the following quotation from an article published in *Cahiers de l'enfance* ('Les Querelles de Vaccination') in which M. Lavarenne, Professor at the Clermont-Ferrand School of Arts, medallist of the *Académie de Médecine*, describes the strange experience sent in by a reader: 'This lady was watching over one of her daughters, a few months old, and not yet vaccinated. She noticed that the child's eyes displayed a black ring around the iris. From her readings in a book on iriscopy she realized that such rings were clear signs of "intoxination". She asked her radiesthetist what the poison was and he "diagnosed" poisoning by Jenner vaccine. A homeopathic dilution of the vaccine caused the black ring to disappear.'

[11] Cf. G. Spencer Brown's critical study in *Revue metapsychique*, 1954.

[12] Cf. C. D. Darlington: *The Facts of Life*, Allen & Unwin, 1953, p. 236 f.: Faking the results of experiments seems to be an easy habit to drop into for those who have little aptitude, but great confidence, in such work. . . . The experiments of Kammerer were probably not faked by Kammerer himself. Those of Michurin and Lysenko . . . were at first not faked at all. At first their errors were largely due to accidents in handling and interpretation. Such accidents are made easy by the experimenters' ignorance of the standard methods of conducting experiments . . . and their over-

powering desire to reach a conclusion which they are certain is the right conclusion, the morally right conclusion, and therefore the only conclusion that any honest man can reach. . . . When the deterrents of scientific criticism are withdrawn the careerist becomes a charlatan overnight. Naturally where ignorance suffices fraud is superfluous. But inevitably ignorance in the master begets fraud in the servant. And, during the last ten years, fraud and ignorance have everywhere marched side by side in expounding the results of Michurin's and Lysenko's work to the public. . . . Fraud was a matter for private enterprise. But now it has been made a State monopoly.'

[13] Cf. The Vatican's injunction: Christians are forbidden to defend opinions which they know to be contrary to faith. They must consider these opinions to be errors with only a false appearance of truth.

[14] *'Soviet biology supplies all of us with arms for the battle.'*

[15] *La lutte idéologique chez les intellectuels,* 1955.

[16] In the same article, M. Garaudy speaks of 'Mendel's empirical observations of his beans' and of 'the 'very limited and modest' conclusions of Mendelism.

[17] Cf. Jean Rostand: *Les Grands Courants de la Biologie* and *L'Atomisme en Biologie.*

2

Biology and the Law

THE layman might not realize that our laws are primarily based on man's natural history. The law is, necessarily, designed by, and for, a specific living species. In this species, reproduction is sexual, the ratio between the sexes is close to unity, fertilization is internal and offspring are produced viviparously. The sexes are distinct from birth, generally remain unchanged throughout life and sexual maturity is only attained after a number of years.

Clearly, if man were an hermaphrodite like the snail; if he changed sex like the mollusc *Crepidula*; if he were born fully developed like the guinea-pig, or if he could grow a new head like the earthworm or the flatworm, our laws would be largely inapplicable. This has been appreciated by many great writers throughout the ages.[1]

But we do not have to leave the real world to learn that in some savage tribes ignorance of elementary biological facts goes hand in hand with special legislation. Thus indigenous Melanesians, who fail to appreciate the causal relation between sexual intercourse and parturition, necessarily organize their families along matriarchal lines.

'At all times,' writes Julliot de la Morandière, 'biological notions have influenced family law. In his recent study of canon law, M. Robert Chabanne has shown that, if most medieval canonists recognized paternal authority in marriage, it was not so much due to scriptural authority – which, on the whole, favours the equality of the sexes – as to the fact that they were steeped in the Germanic tradition which happened to agree with the scientific beliefs of the time. In the Middle Ages, women were thought to be basically akin to animals, the active principle of generation being lodged in the man and his seed. The woman's role was simply restricted to receiving and nurturing man's seed. Woman was above all an *instrumentum*. The increasing part played by woman in modern law[2] and her ever-growing legal independence may be explained by advances in biological knowledge which have led to the rejection of the false views of the Middle Ages.'[3]

To clarify specific points of law, jurists have often been forced to consult biologists and physicians. The editors of the Code Napoléon, for instance, asked Fourcroy (a famous chemist under the Consulate) to fix the extreme limit of pregnancy.[4]

The law having been promulgated for normal men, it has sometimes been embarrassed by certain abnormalities or aberrations which arise spontaneously in the human species.

Speaking of these abnormalities, Isidore Geoffrey Saint-Hilaire has stressed the close relationship between law and physiology; many problems before a court, and particularly the question of sex determination, can never be solved without the advice of a competent physician:

'The laws of all nations recognize that the members of the societies which they govern, are divided into two great classes of individuals on the basis of sex differences. One of these classes is endowed with duties from which the other is exempt, and also with rights of which the other is deprived. Thus from the moment a child's sex is officially recognized, the main course of its life is set; he is fitted into one of the two great classes, whose functions in the family and in society are not only different but almost opposite.

In this respect the law neither allows nor foresees any intermediate possibilities.'

This attitude must strike the physiologist as mistaken, or at least as a crude over-simplification. Some individuals exhibit both male and female characteristics, and, contrary to traditional belief, some of these hermaphrodites simply cannot be fitted into one of the two sexual categories, either because they have undifferentiated sex organs (neutral hermaphroditism) or else because their sexual organs consist of an equal number of male and female parts (mixed hermaphroditism).[5]

Today the question of sex is much more complicated than Isidore Geoffroy Saint-Hilaire could ever have suspected, for the modern biologist considers sexual differences under three largely independent headings: genetic, gonadic, and somatic.

Thus, cases of precocious sex reversal (differences between the genetic and gonadic factors) are known to exist side by side with cases of adult sex reversal in which individuals with female gonads acquire masculine somatic characteristics as a result of suprarenal tumours (differences between the gonadic and somatic factors). Recently a Perthshire Sheriff refused a petition by the Secretary of the Registrar-General's office for authority to make corrected entries in the register in the case of a fifty-year-old father of two children who was said to be changing his sex. The Sheriff held that, assuming a change of sex had taken place, a section of the Registration Act, 1854, could not be invoked to correct the entry of birth as it was directed towards the correction of an entry which was erroneous when the information was given.

Another biological problem to embarrass the lawyer is the

case of the double monster (a single trunk with two heads) resulting from the imperfect division of a single embryo.

What does the Law make of such a creature? Ought it to be considered as one individual or as two? Does it answer to one name or to two? Can it marry?[6] Will it inherit as one person or as two? How can legal sanction be applied in case of a crime committed by one of the pair?

'Lawyers may argue interminably on such questions,' Isidore Geoffroy Saint-Hilaire wrote, 'and on a score of others arising out of them, but, once the scientific facts can be established, the problem is a simple one, so much so that in all countries where double monsters were known, common sense has generally resolved it in the same way: every two-headed double monster, no matter whether with two separate trunks or not, is considered as two individuals, and every double monster with a single head, no matter whether it had two trunks or not, as a *single* individual. . . . The determination of the legal status of a double monster is therefore devoid of any great difficulty. . . . In most legal codes, questions relating to inheritance or to testamentary dispositions are resolved by the simple expedient of counting the heads.'[7]

According to Saint-Hilaire, syncephalic monsters (monsters with a single, compound, head) would confront the Law with further problems. As it happens, this problem is purely academic since all such monsters are either stillborn or live for at most two hours.

Certain types of double monstrosity, and ignorance of their causes, can lead to a great deal of misunderstanding and suffering. Thus a double monster may be the mother's retarded twin brother rather than her offpsring (case of

[58]

foetal inclusion). In unmarried girls, or in women separated from their husbands, this may well give cause for 'certain imputations which the physician ought to put into the right light.'[8]

Even the simple and relatively frequent case of twins has been the subject of legal argument. Primogeniture was of old accorded to the second-born, it being argued that, having been conceived and formed first, it ought to occupy the rear of the uterus. In modern law, however, seniority is accorded to the first-born.

To conclude this list, we might recall that, in the sixteenth and even in the seventeenth centuries, women who gave birth to monsters were cruelly punished for 'having had sexual relations with animals'.

.   .   .   .   .

Nowadays our knowledge of man has advanced so far that such crude errors, based on biological ignorance, need no longer be committed. Even so, exceptional phenomena may still give rise to false interpretations in fact, and hence in law.

If Mrs. Haldane is right in suggesting that parthenogenesis (virgin birth) may occur spontaneously in one out of 100,000 or 1,000,000 births (as happens in turkeys), we can easily foresee that this freak phenomenon may give rise to defamatory accusations.

But parthenogenesis quite apart, it is certain that new biological findings must have inevitable repercussions in the legal field. This influence of biology on the Law is manifold and must be examined from different viewpoints. On the one hand, biology provides jurists with new data by the light it has thrown on the problem of paternity. On the other hand, to the extent that new biological techniques modify human behaviour, i.e. to the extent that biology tends to create an *homo biologicus* with unforeseen attributes, it forces the Law either to discard, or else to modify some of its present attitudes.

Let us first of all examine what new light biology can shed on the legal problem of establishing the paternity of an alleged father.

French law holds that paternity can only be proved when it can be shown that physical contact between the mother and the alleged father took place at the time of conception, which in turn is calculated from the date of birth. Now, since the work of geneticists on the transmission of blood groups, the above method has ceased to be the *only* possible one.

An examination of the blood groups involved (the groups O, A, B, AB, rhesus factors, M and N antigens, etc.) may make it possible to establish a genetic incompatibility between the blood of the child and the blood of the alleged father. Though it is impossible – at least for the moment – to show by serological analysis that a given child is the offspring of a given father, it can sometimes be shown that a given child *cannot possibly be that man's child*.

Let us look at some simple examples.

A child of group A or B cannot have two parents of group O; hence, if the mother belongs to group O, the father cannot. A child of group MN cannot have two parents of group N, hence if the mother belongs to group N, the father cannot. A Rhesus positive child cannot have two Rhesus negative parents; hence if the mother is Rhesus negative, the father cannot be, etc.[9]

In practice, investigations of paternity involve blood tests of the three interested parties: the alleged father, the mother and the child. Such tests are extremely reliable if they are carried out by a competent serologist. There is, of course, a theoretical possibility that a mutation of the gene, in the germinal cells of the parents, may lead to a false diagnosis, but this is extremely improbable. In fact the improbability becomes an impossibility if more than one genetic argument can be mustered in favour of rejecting paternity.[10]

According to André Tétry,[11] the discovery of the Rh factor gives a man wrongly accused of paternity a 50 per cent chance of proving his innocence, while previously his chance was merely 35 per cent. As our knowledge of hereditary blood characters progresses from day to day, it seems likely that there will be an ever-growing number of cases of refuted paternity.

Serological evidence has been accepted by many courts since 1924. At first, French jurists rejected it as being 'contrary to the general trend of French law', in which paternity cannot be established or disproved directly (Tribunal de la Seine, judgement of 12 November 1935), but such evidence has since been accepted unreservedly by the *Tribunals* of Nice (17 November 1937), of Aix (1939, subject to consent by the interested parties), of Lille (1947), of Montpellier (1948) and of Pau (1949).

Moreover, by the Decree of 15 July 1955, Article 340 has been amended to the effect that no affiliation orders can be considered by the courts once blood tests have shown that the defendant cannot be the father of the child.

In general, jurists look upon blood tests as circumstantial

rather than direct evidence. In cases of disputed paternity, blood tests can only be called for by the court after the husband has offered other evidence, e.g. concealment of birth.

'Would it not mean undermining faith in marriage,' Savatier asked, 'if we allowed every husband to challenge his paternity by calling for blood tests? . . . Hence, it is only in certain marginal cases that the law authorizes blood tests as additional evidence.' The Law must protect rather than disturb the social order, and it is 'far better to force an odd illegitimate child upon a couple, than to break down systematically the very walls of the conjugal edifice'.[12]

The question of blood tests is a very delicate one. Such tests must never become coercive, for that would be a violation of the rights of the individual. True, Nerson thinks it is quite intolerable that a defendant should be allowed to refuse a blood test simply because he objects to the personal inconvenience of being pricked with a needle ('the defendant who refuses to submit to a blood test abuses his individual rights'). But even so, all a court can do is to call for a blood test and, in case of refusal, draw its own conclusions.

As Sabatier pointed out, society can never have authority over the human body. This is true, *a fortiori*, of such *private matters* as the question of paternity. 'No doubt, in the case of so harmless an examination as a simple blood test, any refusal to comply may lead the court to suspect a lack of sincerity on the part of the recalcitrant party – it is up to that party to run that risk. But the sanctity of the human body must remain the rule in civil law.'

In any case, all requests for a serological opinion must

come from the courts themselves, since, according to Roger Merle,[13] privately arranged tests may have very serious consequences. By establishing that a given person cannot be the father of a child, the results 'may lead to the most serious upheavals in social and family relations, the disruption of marital harmony, physical violence against the wife, the breaking of emotional bonds between a man and a child both of whom the Law may constrain to continue living under one roof, exclusion of the child from a family from which, under present conditions, it has every right to expect some affection, and the annoying and pointless resentment against a verdict in cases where the scientific refutation of paternity runs counter to a previous legal decision'.

Since even an official blood transfusion centre may have difficulties in keeping information secret (and this despite the fact that such centres are not set up for the purpose of satisfying public curiosity), no private practitioner ought ever to lend himself to this investigation. Not only is there no need for him to do so – the seekers after 'biological truth' are not ill and consequently not in need of his assistance – but moreover, in so doing, he may incur the displeasure of the courts. It is even questionable whether, in the absence of a definite court order, this triple intervention (blood tests of father, mother, and child) is legal, and if it is not an offence under the law governing voluntary mutilations. Furthermore, a disclosure of the results may well be interpreted as a breach of professional secrecy (Article 378 of the French Penal Code).

Merle concludes with the following remarks: 'While it seems right and proper that biological discoveries be given their rightful place in paternity questions, it would be unreasonable and unsettling if we allowed marital doubt, suspicion and anxiety to be unleashed through unauthorized blood tests. If we were to close our eyes to such practices, it will only be a few years before department stores will offer paternity "photomatons" to satisfy the insane curiosity of the crowd. That would serve neither family nor personal interests. "We are driven mad," Nietzsche wrote, "not by doubt but by certainty." '

In England there is not statutory power to compel the parties involved to submit to blood grouping tests. A Select Committee of the House of Lords in 1939 gave its approval to a Bill which would give a defendant in paternity cases the right to insist on blood tests, but the Bill lapsed owing to the outbreak of war. The present position in the courts is that evidence in respect of blood groups is admissible. This evidence should be given by an expert. Incompatibility of these groups may disprove paternity; but compatibility is not accepted as conclusive.[14]

. . . . .

It would, of course, be much better if, side by side with negative tests disproving paternity, there were *positive tests* establishing it. Now this is by no means beyond the means of future serological developments, and would cause a veritable legal upheaval. So long, however, as proofs of paternity do not involve an abrogation of individual rights, Savatier thinks they can only be socially advantageous: 'When paternity ceases to be a mystery, a great social iniquity will have disappeared. Each of the parents will then be faced with equal responsibility for their common child. It will no longer be possible for the man to escape his responsibility since the State will welcome this chance of easing the financial burden of public child assistance.'

[64]

We must remember that in exceptional cases biology can even now adduce positive proof of paternity. This happens when the father has certain rare genetic traits. Thus, Cockayne lists more than one hundred skin conditions alone, for which the genetic background is known. In addition to these, certain skin abnormalities are always inherited from father to son, and never occur in women.[15]

More than twenty years ago a Norwegian woman gave birth to a child with abnormally short fingers. This condition is called brachydactyly (atrophy of the middle phalanx of each finger) and is known to be the result of a dominant genetic factor. This means that brachydactyly is, and can only be, transmitted directly by one of the parents. If the mother is normal, it follows that the father must necessarily be abnormal. Now in this particular case the alleged father happened to be the only man in the area with brachydactyly, and the court, taking the advice of geneticists, found in favour of the mother.[16]

Otto L. Mohr, who reported this incident, observed that the father had one chance in two of not transmitting his abnormality (since he was certain to be heterozygous for this particular gene)[17] but had drawn the wrong card and so branded his child.

. . . . .

Biology has sometimes made possible the legal identification of babies, particularly in cases of substitution. Such cases are reported by Wiener (1933) and Franceschetti (1948).

M.J., father of two twins, Victor and Pierre (aged six years) happened to see a child (Eric V.) in the street with

[65]

a striking semblance to his son Victor. He made inquiries and discovered that young Eric had been born on the same night and in the same maternity ward as his own children. It struck him at once that the babies must have been substituted, and that Eric V. was Victor's identical twin.

At his request, Franceschetti carried out blood tests which established:

1. That Pierre J. could not belong to the J. Family;
2. That Pierre J. could belong to the V. Family;
3. That Eric and Victor, belonging to identical blood groups, were identical twins. This fact was, moreover, corroborated by a skin graft; a small cutaneous section taken from Eric being grafted on Victor, and *vice versa*. The grafts took, which they could not have done had the two boys not been identical twins.[18]

Franceschetti's conclusion was clear: Pierre and Eric, born in the same hospital and on the same night, had been exchanged by mistake. The court, in ordering the return of the children to their respective parents, demonstrated its faith in the findings of biology.

Not so long ago, the French Press raised a clamour about the so-called Roubaix case. A Mme Piesset and a Mme Wahl had both given birth to a child in a clinic of that town on the same night (28 August 1950). The hospital authorities claimed that Mme Wahl had been delivered of a boy and Mme Piesset of a girl.

Mme Wahl immediately protested that there had been a substitution (the midwife had told her that she had helped to deliver a girl), but Mme Piesset insisted that there had been no mistake.

Eventually, Mme Wahl took the matter to court. A long legal battle ensued till blood tests carried out by Dr.

Moullec in 1957, finally gave incontrovertible proof that the children had been substituted. Louise Jeanne could not be the child of the Piessets but could be the child of the Wahls, while Henri could not be the child of the Wahls but could be the child of the Piessets.

As a result the *Tribunal Civil* of Lille (13 June 1957) ordered Louise Jeanne to be returned to her real parents while little Henri – unwanted by the Piesset family – was also allowed to remain with that family who had agreed to look after him.

The court judged 'that it would be detrimental to the physical and moral welfare of little Jeanne Louise if her return to her natural parents were delayed pending an appeal'. It granted M. and Mme Piesset the right to see Louise Jeanne on the first and third Sundays of every month, and also on the second and fourth Thursdays.

This decision so infuriated Mme Piesset, that she made it known that she would oppose its execution by force. Nor was she alone in her resentment, the Press accusing the magistrates of uprooting unfortunate children on the archaic assumption that blood ties are more important than happiness. In fact, no decision the court could have taken would have been satisfactory all round.

In the end (September 1957) it was decided that both children be sent to the same boarding-school at the municipality's expense, the two families sharing the children during their holidays.

This compromise, suggested by M. Provo, Deputy-Mayor of Roubaix, was acceptable to the two families. Thus, at least for the moment, this painful episode is settled, though the legal battle still continues (1960).

To avoid the substitution of children, their identity must

be preserved from the moment of birth. According to C. Sannié, the only effective method is to take the new-born baby's finger-prints, which do not change throughout an individual's life. However, this method presents practical difficulties (clenched fists, shallow ridges, etc.). As an alternative, prints of the soles of the feet can be taken far more easily.

It has also been suggested that a 'seal' be placed on the baby's umbilicus, or that both mother and child be marked with ink that would only be detectable under ultra-violet light, and that would subsequently disappear without leaving a trace.

Speller, in his *Law Relating to Hospitals and Kindred Institutions*, 3rd edn., page 284, says that there appear to be no reported cases on substitution of babies born in an English hospital. If proved an action at law would arise. Whether the hospital authorities would be liable or not would depend upon whether they had lapsed from the standard of reasonable care. The taking of a new born baby's foot-print on a form giving the mother's name and recording first details of the child might be good evidence that the authorities had not been negligent.

.　　　.　　　.　　　.　　　.

Let us now look at some legal problems arising from artificial insemination.

It has always been a basic assumption in law that births result exclusively from physical contact between father and mother. Now biology has changed all that.

No longer will a husband be able to disown a child conceived in his absence, his physical presence at the time being irrelevant (telegenesis). Similarly, the husband's absence at the time of conception is no longer a valid objection to blood tests for investigating his paternity.

Savatier has pointed out that artificial insemination came as a surprise not only to French law, but to the law of other nations as well. A century ago, no lawyer would have foreseen that one day the act of fertilization would be dissociated from cohabitation.

This dissociation faces the lawyer with a great many problems. Though there are hardly any legal difficulties in the case of unmarried mothers, and very few in the case of married women artificially inseminated by their own husbands, the problems are considerable in the case of the married woman who obtains her semen from an anonymous donor (artificial insemination with a donor – A.I.D.).

Now, if the husband does not consent to A.I.D., the woman may be said to have committed adultery, and this is how the Law ought to interpret her action. But even where the husband has given his consent, the Law still holds that adultery has been committed (Article 336 of the *Code Pénal*) and it is by no means certain that the husband may not use this fact in a divorce plea.

Quite apart from that risk, jurists are generally hostile to A.I.D., which they see as foisting a (biologically adulterous) intruder upon the natural family, thus upsetting the social order. In fact, husbands who consent to A.I.D. simply adopt the children of strangers and pass these children off as their own. Their action may have grave social consequences, and doctors cannot be too careful in taking every precaution against possible claims by the married couple, the child, the donor, and even the donor's wife.

[69]

In some countries, doctors insist that the child's future be safeguarded either by a life-insurance policy or else by an adoption order which protects the child from being disinherited on the grounds of his 'adulterous' conception. Sometimes, doctors will insist on choosing a donor of the same blood group as the legal father, thus thwarting any possible proofs of non-paternity by blood tests, and obviating any claims arising in this way. It goes without saying that the 'donor' has no claims whatsoever on the child, all legal rights being vested in the legal father.

In September 1951, it so happened that a Danish woman divorced the legal father to marry the biological father; it is an interesting fact that custody of her child was given to the former.

In *Maclennan* v. *Maclennan* (1958) S.L.T. 12, the Scottish Court of Session held that for adultery to be committed there had to be two parties physically present and engaging in the sexual act at the same time and that artificial insemination did not satisfy this test. On 10 September 1958 the Home Office named the members of the Feversham Committee appointed by the Home Secretary and the Secretary of State for Scotland to inquire into the practice of human artificial insemination and its legal consequences, and to consider whether any change in the law was desirable. This committee is at present still sitting. The Royal Commission on Marriage and Divorce, 1951–5, in its Report (Cmd. 9678 of 1956) recommended in para. 90 that the acceptance by a wife of artificial insemination by a donor without the consent of her husband should be made a new and separate ground of divorce.

Modern genetics have shown that a great many physical and mental abnormalities are transmitted with almost mathematical precision. We have already mentioned the case of brachydactyly, but there are far more serious congenital abnormalities: congenital bone defects, congenital cataract, Huntington's chorea, xeroderma pigmentosum, nervous and muscular degeneration and amaurotic juvenile idiocy. In order to halt the transmission of these genetic defects, a number of countries (twenty-two states of the United States, Germany, Switzerland, *et al.*) have accepted the principle of the preventive sterilization of certain categories of deficients. At the time of writing, more than 50,000 individuals have been sterilized in the United States.

Sterilization is a simple operation that does not impair sexual potency. Though a great number of foreign jurists favour the idea of eugenic sterilization whose, admittedly limited, results would unquestionably have a favourable effect on the biological health of society at large, most French jurists are formally opposed to a procedure which they consider an unwarranted attack on the freedom and dignity of mankind.

In England the opinion given by the Medical Defence Union in 1948 was that sterilization on eugenic grounds alone is illegal, but that it is not so if there are therapeutic reasons. The patient's consent, and also that of his spouse, should first be obtained; see *Law and Ethics for Doctors*, by Hadfield, at page 197 (Eyre & Spottiswoode, 1958). In *Bravery* v. *Bravery* in 1954 it was said that sterilization of the male is illegal. Stephen's *Digest of Criminal Law* asserts that castration is mayhem.

In France, eugenic legislation is still restricted to the

half-hearted and almost pointless measure of a 'prenuptial medical examination', the only concession to Louise Hervieu's long and courageous battle.

According to Article 63 of the *Code Civil* (amended by the statute of 2 November 1945) every candidate for marriage must present the marriage officer with a medical certificate. But that is, in fact, all there is to it. Candidates with unsatisfactory certificates are not precluded from marriage, nor are such candidates legally bound to communicate the contents of their certificates to their future marriage partners. The examination is absolutely secret, and it is left entirely to the candidate's own conscience and sense of responsibility to take what steps he chooses. Savatier points out that this is characteristic of the basic attitude of French law.

Any acceptance of enforced eugenics would be tantamount to 'giving the state virtual control over what is most specifically personal in the human body, and what mankind has consequently looked upon as the most inviolable attribute of individuality. Man would no longer be treated as a person, but as an instrument for propagating and improving a race which in turn would be controlled absolutely by the State.'

Nerson, too, condemns all measures of this kind: 'No matter what the political system, all eugenic measures imposed by force strike us as reprehensible. Medical dictatorship is no better than political dictatorship; we can only allow voluntary eugenics. . . .'

And in the same vein: 'Even if such measures should one day prove perfectly justified from a scientific point of view, we should nevertheless remain opposed to their implementation; we fully agree that it is regrettable that individuals tainted with hereditary defects should be granted the right of procreation, but how can we go further than voluntary eugenics, that simply appeal to the patient's good sense and conscience, without establishing a medical police system that would be an attack on human liberty?'

J. Carbonnier is a little less emphatic: 'Being rooted in psychology, our matrimonial laws give no consideration to biological, physical, facts. No doubt, this attitude is a relic of the canonical aversion to these facts. The human body never entered into the *Code civil*, as it were. In the *Code*, man is a purely spiritual being. Apart from the determination of the legal age of puberty, there is no further mention of the part played by the human body in marriage. . . .

'But biology may not have spoken its last word, and may well prove to be a progressive factor that will set the tone for conjugal institutions of the future. Scientific advances, like scientific abuses, have confronted the modern world with new problems concerning not only the health but also the purity of the race, and these problems must surely be reflected in our matrimonial laws. During the years of the Occupation, Frenchmen knew how to resist the contagion of German racialism in the field of marriage, but they may find it far more difficult to reject the idea of eugenic measures.'

If most French jurists obstinately cling to their opposition to eugenic ideas, it is not so much because they dislike the limited measures geneticists are trying to introduce, as because of their fear of the excesses to which a 'biological' conception of the law might lead once the frail barrier still protecting the individual against collective pressure is let down.

Some geneticists, like H. J. Muller in America, have gone

[73]

so far as to suggest such *positive* eugenic measures as the artificial insemination of female volunteers with semen from superior individuals. Now, justified though his suggestion may be by genetic considerations, it must be conceded that such 'veterinary' procreation must strike many as scandalous.

'The inviolability of the person, the liberty of the individual, the sacred nature of their intimacy, have already lost, for the modern juristic conscience, a great deal of their meaning. The rights of the individual seem to be dissolving in the evergrowing rights of society, and if these rights were ever to be administered by an "inspired" dictator, with a mission to fashion a new humanity by applying the findings of modern biology, he might stop short of nothing.'

And Savatier goes on to say:

'Already, biologists have established that, with methodical organization of artificial insemination, one virile donor can fertilize 20,000 women annually. Is there any reason why some biologically inspired dictator should not organize the selection of "élite donors" by the sterilization of all other males? That would spell the end of marriage, and all that is human, moral and judicial in it. . . .'

On a smaller scale, however, physicians, and particularly French physicians, have long been denouncing the danger of consanguineous marriages, and have clamoured for legal sanctions against them. Such marriages are genetically harmful since they encourage the expression of recessive or latent genes. In the offspring of such unions, the rate of certain defects (albinism, deaf-mutism, etc.) is appreciably greater than in the offspring of normal unions.

'Since marriages contracted between relatives have the sad privilege of afflicting their unfortunate children with

[74]

the gravest of infirmities, we may be permitted to view such marriages as infractions of public hygiene, and we are bound to point this out to the public legislators. . . . It seems incredible that, when we display so much solicitude for the welfare of our children (and it is mainly with an eye to child welfare that the *Code civil* speaks of the indissolubility of marriage), the Law should not be primarily concerned with ensuring their chief good, i.e. their health.'[19]

It would take us too far afield to discuss the question of enforced birth-control in detail. We shall merely examine the specific case of the mother who has contracted German measles during the first weeks of pregnancy. Now the virus responsible for that disease has a strong teratogenic effect on the embryo so that there there is every chance of an abnormal child being born. In these circumstances, can there be any objection to an induced abortion which, in France at least, is illegal except where pregnancy carries a mortal risk for the mother?[20]

The *Académie de Médecine* has, in fact, appointed a commission to go into this very question and has also consulted members of the *Académie des Sciences morales et politiques*, jurists, and leading personalities in other fields. At this stage, there may still be some doubt about the correct answer, since the birth of an abnormal child is merely a probability. However, if future diagnostic developments should turn this probability into certainty, have we the right to let abnormal children be born into the world?

.   .   .   .   .

A host of legal problems is also posed by skin grafting, i.e. the transplanting of an organ or a tissue from one individual

[75]

either to another part of the same individual (autoplastic grafting), or else to another individual (homoplastic grafting). Legal difficulties arise mainly in the case of homoplastic grafts for which no restitution in kind can ever be made.

It goes without saying that skin grafts must never be performed without the donor's full consent, which means that 'the donor must be fully advised what part of his body is to be removed, and what consequences such removal may have on his health, and furthermore, that he is told to what use to which the fragment he has provided will be put' (Savatier).

In any case, the whole business is studded with legal difficulties since 'doctors, who are the only persons permitted to mutilate the human body, are given that mandate specifically for curative purposes, and not for weighing up the damage to one body against the health of another, no matter if the mutilation is performed with the donor's consent'.[21]

The underlying legal principle here, as in the cases of artificial insemination and voluntary sterilization, is the belief that the Law must defend the individual from himself, and that, even where he consents to such experiments, he does not thereby make his action less indictable.

For the time being, homoplastic grafts are carried out very exceptionally, since they are generally unsuccessful, except between identical twins, and in the case of some embryonic organs (brephoplastic grafts).

However, with improvements in grafting techniques, it is likely that homoplastic grafts will become more and more the order of the day. This day may well have been brought nearer by the American biologist G. Snell's discovery of an 'enhancing substance' which helps the organism to over-come its specificity. Also, Medawar's experiments have shown that embryos can be treated in such a way as to develop lasting tolerance towards homoplastic grafts.

Brephoplastic grafts, taken from stillborn children or premature foetuses, raise special legal problems concerning the rights and conditions of removal. The same is true of corneal grafts (kerato-plastic grafts) which have become so common[22] that the Law has been forced to restrict the interval in which the removal may be carried out to eight hours after death (Decree of 2 October 1947). Moreover, by the decree of 7 July 1949, such operations have now been legalized 'whenever the deceased has, by testamentary disposition, bequeathed[23] his eyes either to a public institution or to a private charity.[24]

Difficulties may arise when the deceased's family are opposed to the removal of the eyes. It seems doubtful if the machinery of the Law can be set into motion quickly enough to force them to comply with the provisions of the will, though in that case the charity or institution in question could take action for damages against the person or persons responsible.[25]

Heated legal arguments have been carried on even about the far more straightforward question of blood-transfusion. Human blood being a living tissue, 'a part of the body', it is not a 'possession' and can therefore not be sold. The donor may be indemnified but he cannot be paid. Moreover, in France blood transfusions may only be carried out by public institutions (1954). Since no one can be compelled to give his blood, Savatier stresses that the Decree of 14 April 1954, whereby certain categories of military

[77]

conscript can be forced to donate their blood, constitutes a strange and rather dangerous exception.[26]

Aurel David has drawn attention to the fact that the grafting of organs constitutes a violation of the personality, and to the equivocal legal aspects of methods which, from any point of view, mean treating living objects as goods and chattels.

What, for instance, happens to the recipient? Does he become a changed person?[27] Can it be said that the personality remains unchanged so long as the brain remains intact? Remember that the endocrine glands, by the effects of their secretions, affect man's emotions and reactions, and that, in Carrel's words, 'man thinks, loves, suffers, admires and prays not only with his brain but with all his organs'. Moreover, how can we be absolutely certain that the brain itself remains unaffected by the biological interference of grafting?[28]

According to Aurel David, we cannot even be sure that the personality remains unaffected when foreign substances are introduced into the human body (prosthesis). The effects of prosthesis, just like hormone therapy, plastic surgery, the erasure of finger-prints and changes in sex, leads to difficulties of legal identification. What becomes of the personality in the course of these processes? Is not the real, identifiable substratum which bears the proper name, in danger of dissolving?

David saw the following dilemma: either we must give up the concept 'person' in favour of an aggregate of parts or else we must hold on to it by defining it more precisely than by external appearance.

Since the Law cannot relinquish the 'individual', David thinks that it is bound to separate personality from the biological body, and to postulate the existence of a central, continuous, indivisible person which owns it.

Untenable though it seems to be, David's interpretation has the merit of bringing us face to face with that 'split' of the physical personality which is the unavoidable consequence of recent biological advances.

.   .   .   .   .

In our cursory examination of the relationship between biology and the Law, we have seen that biology was able not only to provide the jurist with new data, but also to suggest new legislation. By supplying a new physiological picture of man, by making it possible, for instance, to dissociate the sexual act from the act of fertilization, to graft parts from one person to the next, biology has forced jurists either to modify the existing laws or else to pass new legislation.

This progress of biology is continuing all the time. To cite just a few of the future possibilities: pregnancy *in vitro* (ectogenesis) would completely change all our notions of *maternity*, no matter whether ectogenesis is total (starting with the fertilized ovum) or partial (starting with the ovum in a more or less advanced stage of development). The day that ectogenesis becomes a practical reality,[29] 'it will have become meaningless to say that Paul is the son of Jack and Susan; in the final analysis there will no longer be room for the entities which these names are supposed to designate' (Gabriel Marcel).

And what would happen to our notion of maternity, the day that a fertilized ovum or a young embryo can be transplanted from one woman to another? (This is already being done in the case of some female mammals.) If a woman gave birth to a child that is not genetically her own, would the real mother be the woman who nourished and bore the foetus, or she who provided the germ cell?[30] Clearly, biology can dissociate the act of maternity, just as it can dissociate the act of paternity.[31]

We know that the spermatozoon has a double function: fertilization and transmission of hereditary characters. Now, by gynogenesis (a type of parthenogenesis stimulated by spermatozoa) we can already produce offspring that owe nothing to the father except the fertilizing stimulus,[32] the father playing no part in the transmission of genes. (Not to mention Michurin genetics, according to which a number of spermatozoa can take part in the creation of a single individual, which in consequence, would have a number of genetic fathers!)

There is, moreover, the case of triploidy (by which individuals may be produced who, genetically speaking, are two parts mother and one part father), and also the development of ova in which the maternal nucleus has been replaced by the nucleus of an embryo of the same species (Briggs and King's method). The product, in that case, is no longer the mother's child, or, at least, she has provided no more than the cytoplasm. The child is largely the offspring of the embryo providing the nucleus, or rather its 'retarded brother' or younger twin.

Then there is the case of androgenesis by which individuals are born who, having only paternal chromosomes, are almost the exclusive offsprings of their father. And finally, there is the well-known case of parthenogenesis, where the offspring is exclusively the mother's child.

Parthenogenesis in the human species is already within the realms of possibility. Since neither husband nor any other man is involved, it might well be called 'auto-adultery'. This is what Savatier had to say on the subject: 'If the all-powerful prophets of biology were ever to advance to the point where parthenogenesis could, in the service of the hypothetical improvement of the human race, become a reality, not only marriage but also paternity and maternity would disappear from the legal horizon. Though the whole thing seems absurd, modern history has shown us that, socially speaking, the absurd can no longer be considered the impossible. What is more, the implementation of the absurd seems to haunt the minds of some scientists.'

The list of biological advances(?) that are bound to cause headaches amongst jurists can be prolonged even further: the preservation of semen by which a man can already produce offspring years and even centuries after his own death;[33] hormone therapy whereby an individual's sex can be changed and whereby puberty can be forced or delayed; chilling techniques which make it possible to keep individuals in a state of latent life for an indefinite period; the use of 'mutagenes' for creating possible new human races; intra-uterine treatment of foetuses whereby basic changes in individual traits can be brought about pre-natally; to mention only a few.

If the latest experiments of Jacques Benoît and his collaborators (Pierre Leroy, Roger and Colette Vendrely) are confirmed, *directed mutations* – which have already been produced in bacteria – will also become feasible in mammals through the action of D.N.A. (desoxyribonucleic acid), a chromosome extract.[34] By extrapolating the results obtained from ducks, we can foresee how, by means of the D.N.A. obtained from a subject A, certain traits of A can be transferred to the reproductive cells of a subject B. This transfer is known as 'chemical hybridization', though, in the case of human beings, it might well be called 'chemical adultery'.

It also seems that, by means of D.N.A., an individual's hereditary traits can be changed post-natally. With some little imagination, one can see standard doses of D.N.A. being administered to every individual, thus endowing him with the most favourable physical and mental traits. All of us would then become supermen, and the children of any one couple would be, strictly speaking, the children of the entire species.

Then there is the problem of sex changes. Ever since biology first discovered ways of changing man's sexual morphology and physiology, many demands for such changes have been received from men and women who claim that they are the victims of an error of nature. 'In the last few years, there have been many instances of men asking for the surgical removal of their genitals, if need be by endocrine or plastic treatment. . . . In all these cases, the men concerned have been of normal physique and not pseudo-hermaphrodites or true hermaphrodites.' [35]

According to Jean Vague, changes of sex are as easy to perform as appendicectomies, and 'in our own country alone thousands of requests (for changes of sex) are received'.[36]

This is not the place for discussing the extent to which the intellectual and aesthetic climate of our age is responsible for this 'transsexualist' neurosis. It is, however, a fact that this neurosis exists, and that to some extent it is encouraged by biological advances.

Some doctors have, in fact, thought that a number of patients might derive benefits from the operation. Thus,

Hamburger, with the authority of the Danish Home Office, performed a therapeutic hormonal and surgical castration of a male transsexualist involving the removal of his penis, plastic surgery on the scrotum, electrolytic depilation of the beard, etc.

In France, for the moment at least, castration is considered inadmissible in law, not only because of the illegality of operation itself, but also because of the problems of the consequent change of identity.[37]

Clearly, as biology turns man into an ever more 'artificial' product, his laws must be fitted to his new state, these laws, as we have made clear, having been promulgated for *homo sapiens* and not for *homo biologicus*.

It may well be asked if this 'biologization' of man has not gone far enough, and if it is not high time that a stop be put to it. This, indeed, seems to be the opinion of a number of jurists, who do not hide their disquiet or their determination to oppose this trend: 'Are we fully aware of the hidden threats to our values and to our legal system that are being hatched out in laboratories and scientific institutions? Do we fully realize their import?

'At present, man's conquest of ever more immense forces of nature is about to bring about an upheaval whose depth it is difficult to plumb. . . .

'When they tamper with animal life, are biologists not secretly haunted by a sublime intoxication? Do they not think that, through animals, they can discover man, the summit of the evolution of life? Almost on the point of having discovered the secrets of animal life, the boldest of them are already itching to shape the lives of our entire species. . . .

'It therefore behoves the jurist to take a stand. It is up to him to safeguard those subjective rights of the individual without which our objective laws would no longer merit their name. . . . It is not up to biology to direct the law, but up to the law to direct the uses to which biology is to be put' (Savatier).

And this is what Nerson has to say: 'While it holds out a promise, each scientific discovery also bears a danger. . . . In assessing the value of science, the jurist, as every other humanist, owes it to himself to preserve a sense of proportion; science may serve him as a guide but never as a model; the ultimate purpose of the law is to establish order. . . . When G. Renard wrote that biology is not a law-giver, he stated a truth that is valid to this day.'[38]

The clash between biology and the Law is, in some respects, fundamental. It may be conceded that, while the biologist is sometimes inclined to look upon man as a purely physical entity, a protoplasmic aggregate of skin, flesh and blood, the jurist sees him in all his physical, spiritual, moral and social complexity.[39] One could therefore agree with Savatier that the jurist's view of man is by far the richer.

It is no over-simplification to say that biologist and jurists sometimes appear as the protagonists of two different, but equally respectable attitudes, between which it is difficult to make a choice. It is hard to tell who is more humane, more idealistic, and more moral – he who rejects eugenics on principle as being a violation of individual liberty and dignity, or he who is opposed to the transmission of organic defects and who would save future generations from the inevitable suffering, diseases and misery it brings in its train.[40]

It seems quite probable that this legal sensitivity to biological changes is the reflection of the 'mean' sensitivity

[84]

of a given social group, the reflection, as it were, of the social super-ego. Moreover, jurists certainly play a beneficial role in delaying the introduction of certain scientific methods which, while quite acceptable in the end, cannot be sprung on an ill-prepared and reluctant public.

But if jurists are on solid ground when, as defenders of individual liberty, they oppose all such coercive measures as the compulsory sterilization of certain defectives, their position becomes weakened when they anathematize all new scientific discoveries and the potential benefits such discoveries can bestow on man.

While we must concede their agitation at new methods that attack the very roots of our traditional notions of maternity, paternity, and individuality, we must also realize that no protests will ultimately be able to halt the march of science. Whether we like it or not, whether we desire it or not, whether the consequences are good or bad, it seems that biology will provide women with the means of having fatherless children in the near future, and that, when that time comes, there are bound to be certain women – and not the worst or the best of them either – who will wish to avail themselves of this new method.

Once they have made up their minds, no legal protests will be able to stop them from practising 'virgin maternity', and while the first of these virgin mothers might shock public opinion, they, just like the first women who submitted to artificial insemination or practised painless childbirth, will not remain alone for long. Similarly nothing will stop people from improving the physical or mental stature of their children by a suitably chosen dose of D.N.A.

All the same, even here, legal solicitude may continue to fulfil a salutary function. Though the law must eventually accept scientific achievements as accomplished facts, it will still have to protect the citizen by prescribing the way in which these new tools are to be applied. It will still be the Law's function – and this is no mean task – to defend and protect the individual, every least part of whom deserves the respect that is due to the whole.

In brief, while the Law will have no option but to bow down before biological fact, it need not relinquish one iota of the humanist spirit with which it is suffused, and continue its noble role of preserving respect for the traditional values of human liberty and dignity.

ESSAY II

REFERENCES

[1] Thus, André Maurois' 'Erophages' (*Nouveaux Discourses du docteur O'Grady*) do not allow swimmers to bare their shoulders, lest they display the aphrodisiac glands on their arms.

[2] Women have not as yet achieved complete emancipation at English law. Sweeping constitutional changes have been effected by various measures such as the Sex Disqualification (Removal) Act, 1919, and the Life Peerages Act, 1958 (which permitted women to take a limited place in the House of Lords for the first time). Important legal changes have been brought about by the Married Women's Property Act, 1882, and the Law Reform (Married Women and Tortfeasors) Act, 1935, which constitutes a married woman in all respects as if she were a *feme sole*. Despite this there are curious restrictions on the ultimate principle of legal equality between the sexes. Some of these were dealt with by Lord Denning in a lively lecture on The Rights of Women published in *The Changing Law* by Stevens in 1953.

[3] The ancient Greeks were less perturbed by their mothers' than by their fathers' death, since they, too, believed in the male's biological supremacy (*see Eumenides* of Aeschylus).

[4] He fixed these between 186 and 286 days (*see* Locre, *Législation civile*, vol. VI, p. 50; Fenet, vol. X, p. 13). In modern French law the limit is fixed between 180 and 300 days. In England judicial notice is taken of the fact that in the ordinary course of nature delivery occurs in, or about, nine months from fruitful intercourse. Judicial notice is also taken of the fact that the normal course is not always taken in nature, and that the actual period may be considerably less or considerably more than the normal mean period of 275–280 days. The least period considered by the English courts was a period of gestation which could not have exceeded 174 days. This was in *Clark* v. *Clark* (1939) 2 All E.R. 59. The longest period admitted as possible by a majority of the House of Lords was in *Preston Jones* v. *Preston Jones* (1951) 1 All E.R. 124. Here it was held that the court was not entitled to assume judicial notice that a child born 360 days after the last coitus between husband and wife was not the child of the husband.

[5] When the nature of hermaphroditism was not yet understood, married people of indeterminate sex were executed for 'profaning the sacrament of marriage'.

[6] If a double monster were to have a child, and 'if each fraction of the monster were to claim the child as its own, forensic medicine would be faced with an utterly insoluble problem' (Dr. Martin: *Histoire des Monstres depuis l'antiquité jusqu'à nos jours*, Reinwald, 1880).

[7] According to Sauval (*Histoire des antiquités de Paris*, vol. II p. 564), a double monster who had stabbed a man to death, was reprieved because of the innocence of one of his constituent persons. This happened in the seventeenth century. Dr. Martin is of the opinion that such clemency was ill-advised: 'The monster ought not to have been reprieved, for, had it turned into an habitual criminal, the law would have born the full responsibility' (ibid., p. 187).

[8] See *De la Duplicité monstreuse par inclusion*, by Dr. Lachèse, Paris, 1823.

[9] This is only approximately true of Rhesus factors, but we cannot here enter into a detailed discussion of the very complex facts involved.

[10] The validity of these genetic demonstrations may well be reduced by increases in the rate of mutation due to the use of atomic energy.

[11] *Le système sanguin Rhesus*, Albin Michel, 1950.

[12] Napoleon said that the State had no interest whatever in challenging the affiliation of illegitimate children.

[13] *Recueil Dalloz*, 20 November 1952.

[14] For the medical value of such tests *see* vol. 9 of *The British Encyclopaedia of Medical Practice*, 2nd edn., at p. 480, and *see also* an article, 'Blood Groups in Affiliation Cases', 98 J.P.N. 355.

[15] *Inherited Abnormalities of the Skin and its Appendages*, O.U.P., 1933.

[16] *Heredity and Disease*, Noron & Co., N.Y., 1934.

[17] Subjects who are homozygous for brachydactyly are not viable.

[18] This statement is not strictly correct. In very exceptional cases skin grafts can take between dizygotic twins. (See p. 101.)

[19] Chazarin, *These*, Montpellier, 1859.

[20] Sweden has legalized abortion in cases of German measles contracted during pregnancy. The matter in England is to a large extent governed by section 58 of the Offences Against the Person Act, 1861, and by the Infant Life (Preservation) Act, 1929. By the former measure it is a felony for any person unlawfully to administer or cause to be administered any poison or other noxious thing or to use any instrument or other means to any woman whether pregnant or not with intent to procure miscarriage. In *R. v. Bourne* (1939) 1 K.B. 687, it was held that an abortion considered necessary in the interests of the mother's mental health was lawful.

[21] In June 1957, American surgeons asked leave of the Massachusetts Supreme Court to authorize Leonard Marsden, aged

nineteen years, to donate one of his kidneys to his twin brother Leon. In giving its consent, the court protected all the parties concerned against any civil or criminal actions that might have resulted from the operation.

22 Physiologists are still not agreed whether kerato-plastic grafts are true grafts. It seems that the cells of the grafted cornea do not survive as such, but are replaced by autonomous cells.

23 Savatier has pointed out that only movable or immovable property can be legally 'bequeathed'. The eyes not falling into either category, the term is misleading.

24 The French Eye-Bank, founded in October 1948 by the *Association des mutilés des yeux de guerre*, has so far registered 8,000 bequests of eyes. More than 2,000 grafts have already been performed. In the United States, the *Eye Bank for Sight Restoration* (N.Y.), in existence since 1936, receives fifty promises of eyes every month.

25 The State of New York requires the formal consent of the next of kin, even when the disposal of the eyes is stipulated in a written will. In England corneal grafting operations were placed on a regular legal basis by the Corneal Grafting Act, 1952. The Act provides that if any person expresses a request in writing, or at any time orally in the presence of two or more witnesses that his eyes be used for therapeutic purposes, then the party lawfully in possession of the body after death may authorize the removal of the eyes from the body for use for those purposes.

26 *See* the official debate on blood transfusion under the chairmanship of Prof. Moureau (15 March 1953) in *Aspects médico-légaux de la transfusion sanguine*, September 1954.

27 Medawar's work has shown that mammalian tolerance to homoplastic grafts may produce veritable monster cells.

28 'The science of the future,' Dr. Paul Chauchard wrote, 'offers us much food for philosophical thought. . . . Once organs can be grafted, the term "individual" becomes much more difficult to define, particularly if cerebral grafts should ever become a possibility. Such grafts would establish beyond any

doubt that the brain plays a paramount role in creating the basic individuality of every organism.'

[29] The culture of separate organs has become laboratory practice since Etienne Wolff's work on the culture of embryonic chick organs *in vitro*.

[30] Moricard has suggested that, in cases of blocked Fallopian tubes an ovum could be taken from the woman's ovary and be introduced into her, or even another woman's, uterus.

[31] The act of maternity is, in fact, dissociated whenever a baby is fed by anyone but its mother. For Ambroise Paré, a mother is no more than a 'half-mother' if she fails to breast-feed her own child.

[32] Giard has already stressed the 'dissociation of our notion of paternity' (Proceedings of the *Société de Biologie*, 25 April 1903): 'If we use the term "paternity" to designate the totality of the acts by which a male determines the creation of a new individual with the co-operation of a female, this totality is not an indivisible whole. It can be dissociated into a series of more or less independent acts, many of which can be performed by different individuals, to each of which a part in this collective paternity may be attributed.'

[33] A young American biologist has apparently used preserved semen, taken from her husband after his death, to provide her with two children.

[34] Cf. *Modifications induites chez les canards Pekin de canard khaki Campbell injecté après la naissance*, La Presse medicale, 9 October 1957.

[35] *See* the article by J. Delay, P. Deniker, R. Volmat, and J. M. Alby in *L'Encéphale*, 1956, pp. 41–80. 'Transsexualists' must be distinguished from transvestitists or homosexuals as neurotics with specific hysterical and narcissistic symptoms.

[36] *La Presse médicale*, 23 May 1956.

[37] By French law, any surgically induced changes of sex can be interpreted as castrations. In that case, by article 316 of the *Code pénal*, the penalty may be transportation with hard labour for life,

or even capital punishment, should death ensue within forty days of the crime.

[38] *Le Droit, l'Ordre et la Raison*, Sirey, 1927.

[39] 'The legal institution of marriage with all its moral, spiritual and poetic connotations, is more truly human than artificial insemination, the transmutation of sex, or parthenogenesis . . .' (Savatier).

[40] The removal of an organ for grafting purposes may also lead to the unhappy choice between respect for the dead and the welfare of a living person. F. Rauh (*Études de morale*, 1911) predicted that welfare considerations would win out in the end.

3

The Singularities of Man

ABOUT two hundred years ago, Voltaire, in an essay on the singularities of nature, examined some of the intriguing facts of natural history which were then arousing the curiosity of his contemporaries. In particular, he discussed the reproductive method of the sweet-water polyp, the snail's withdrawal into its shell, the existence of queen bees, and the presence of shell deposits on mountaintops. True, the illustrious writer's conclusions are not altogether pertinent, because Voltaire, though he had a great deal of common sense, went in such great fear of being duped that he frequently sinned by excess of suspicion, refusing to accept any facts that savoured of the fantastic.

I have taken the liberty of paraphrasing Voltaire's title to apply it to such oddities or eccentricities of the human species which, quite apart from being captivating digressions of nature, give the biologist and the physician much food for thought.

Amongst these 'singularities' of man we shall not discuss the innumerable results of genetic mutations. In other words, we shall ignore people with six fingers, porcupine men, glass men, rubber men, giants, women with supernumerary breasts, men without hair, teeth, sweat glands, men with black urine, and so on. Instead, we shall concentrate on those human peculiarities which, by some infraction of man's fundamental biological mechanism, violate the ordinary laws of our species. In short, we shall merely consider what Sir Francis Galton, in speaking of twins, called an 'experiment of nature'.

Identical Twins

Identical twins might well be called one of nature's classical and relatively frequent experiments. Let us recall that there are two types of twins: pluri-ovular twins (arising from two or more ova) who are called fraternal twins, and uni-ovular twins (arising from a single ovum) who are known as identical twins.

Twinning, fraternal or identical, is an exception to the normal cycle of the human species which, unlike the dog and the cat, is uniparous.

The case of pluri-ovular twins which seems to result from a superabundance of gonado-tropic hormones, can hardly be called an experiment of nature. In any case, such twinning can easily be induced artificially in uniparous animals (sheep, cow) by appropriate hormonal treatment. In this connexion we might mention the recent case of the birth of quintuplets to a couple treated for stubborn sterility.

The biologist is far more interested in identical twins as an exceptional example of natural polyembryony in our species. Considerably rarer than pluri-ovular twins, uni-ovular twins occur once in every three hundred ova, and the known cases of uni-ovular triplets, quadruplets and quintuplets are very much rarer still. The striking resemblance of identical twins need not surprise us since, according to Dr. Apert's happy phrase, they are but the reprints of one and the same individual.

Professor Sannié has reported the case of two identical twins in America whose resemblance was so great that their mother could only identify them by having their finger-prints taken, and Pascal must certainly have been thinking of identical twins when he wrote that 'two similar faces, neither of which is particularly amusing by itself, may amuse by their resemblance'.

Whenever two uni-ovular embryos do not fully separate, we have double monsters or Siamese twins – hence Etienne Wolff's comment that identical twins are but the result of double monstrosity carried to the extreme.

Let us recall that polyembryony, so exceptional in human beings, is the normal state of certain species of mammals. Thus the female of the armadillo (a small American edentate) lays a single egg which gives birth to a number of embryos (four in the case of the Texas armadillo and eight to twelve in the case of the Argentinian armadillo). Similarly, the egg of the worm *Lumbricus trapezoides* generally gives birth to two individuals, and in bryozoa (small aquatic invertebrates) one egg produces hundreds of larvae. The same is true of some insects.

Polyembryony in the human species – or for that matter in the armadillo – is not, as was previously thought, the result of the ovum's first division (blastomere), but occurs during a later stage of embryonic development. It is completely unknown why this embryonic duplication takes place in certain ova. Some have blamed it on hormonal deficiencies; others, like Fournier, have blamed syphilitic infections; others again have put the blame on various viruses. Be that as it may – all that we can say with certainty is that certain human families have a genetic tendency to produce identical twins, and that this tendency is transmitted particularly by the male progenitor.

In a number of animals, polyembryony can be produced experimentally by various means, e.g. by the mechanical fractionation of the germ, or by the action of appropriate chemical substances. Etienne Wolff and Hubert Lutz dissected the embryonal disk of a duck to obtain up to five embryos from one and the same germ cell. These methods do not prove effective in all animals, but where they are, we can conclude that a given ovum has much vaster potentialities than it normally displays.

Even without having carried out similar experiments on the human ovum – and for very good reasons, too! – we know from nature's own twinning experiment that the human germ has such potentialities to a high degree. We know that if, by one method or another, we managed to divide the human ovum, each fragment will be able to produce what the normal ovum produces under ordinary conditions. Thus the famous case of the Dionne quintuplets has the same biological significance as Hubert Lutz and Etienne Wolff's laboratory experiments. From the Dionne quintuplets we know with certainty that the human ovum has the same polyembryonic potential as the duck's egg, and that it differs from the eggs of certain ascidians or insects which lack that potential.

From nature's experiments on identical twins, we know, furthermore, that in our species, the fertilized egg is sex-determined: identical twins are always of the same sex, while fraternal twins may or may not be. Actually, this proof is no longer crucial since we have a great deal of other convincing evidence in favour of precocious sex-determination. But fifty years before the advent of genetics, this argument was part of the stock in trade of biologists. We shall not dwell on any other points of interest arising from this 'experiment of nature', except to mention that by providing individuals with perfectly alike hereditary traits, nature enables us to make clearer distinctions between the respective influences of heredity and environment.

Dextrocardia

Another, less common, but very interesting abnormality – an abnormality within an abnormality, we might say – is the general inversion of the internal organs.

Dextrocardia is, in effect, not uncommon in double monsters, where the heart of one of the pair has its axis inclined towards the right, the apex lying below the right nipple instead of the left. This positional inversion entails a functional inversion, the left side receiving de-oxygenated blood and the right side receiving oxygenated blood. Other thoracic and abdominal organs are similarly inverted, the right lung with its three lobes occupying the left part of the rib cage, while the left lung with its two lobes occupies the right. The liver is on the left and so are the ascending colon, the caecum and the appendix, while the spleen and the descending colon are on the right. In short, the internal organs have become the mirror images of their normal position. Spectacular though this abnormality is, it causes little inconvenience, provided only that it is complete.

According to Eichwald, organic inversion is usually found in all double monsters that are joined at the thorax and generally affects the left partner only. In identical human twins, it sometimes happens that while one of the twins has his organs inverted, the other one has not. Furthermore, marks of mirror symmetry so often found in identical twins, are frequently taken as minor signs of organic inversion (the hair whorls growing clockwise and anti-clockwise respectively; moles or birthmarks on the right or left cheeks respectively, etc.). Also, Spemann and Falkenburg's experiments on *Tritons*, have shown that artificially induced twins have an abnormally high rate of organ inversion.

Moreover, it is believed that in the case of human organ inversion, a normal twin may have perished in the embryonic state, so that every person with such an inversion would be the sole survivor of a pair of identical twins. As regards the incidence of this abnormality, radiologists' estimates vary between one in four thousand and one in forty thousand. Six hundred and fifty cases have so far been mentioned in medical literature.

Human Chimeras

Nature's experiment with identical twins, by being the exception to the rule, has the further advantage of allowing us to verify the law of individual specificity. According to that law, organs cannot be transferred successfully from one individual to another.

All human beings behave as if their tissues suffered from a type of super-patriotism verging on xenophobia. Now grafting between identical twins is tolerated precisely because they are, in effect, one and the same human being and because in their case homoplastic grafts are tantamount to autoplastic grafts. The fact that a kidney could successfully be grafted from Richard Herrick to his identical twin Ronald (Boston, 1943), shows how great an asset an identical twin can be, representing as he does a ready supply of organs for emergencies – on condition, of course, that the twin is willing to make the sacrifice. It is reported that a certain Madeira crossed half the world in an aeroplane to bring a few square centimeters of skin to his twin brother who had been severely injured in the legs and abdomen. Madeira was the only man in the whole world who could provide this vital bit of tissue. In forensic medicine, this graft tolerance of identical twins has occasionally been used for identifying babies substituted in maternity wards.

Now Medawar – the famous specialist on animal grafts – recently found that it might be possible to induce graft tolerance even between fraternal twins. In a series of brilliant experiments he showed that animals such as mice could be made to tolerate grafts by, for instance, injecting cells from a mouse B into the embryo of mouse A. Skin post-natally grafted from B to A will live, and this would certainly not have been the case if the embryo had not been treated or 'educated' in this way.

These experiments have not yet been applied medically, but already some immunologists are weighing the possibilities of inducing tolerance to a particular donor – father or mother for instance – in the human embryo, so that all human beings could share in the advantages now enjoyed exclusively by identical twins.[1]

Be that as it may, this experiment of inducing graft-tolerance in embryos is, in fact, performed by nature herself in twin calves, where spontaneous grafts among pluri-ovular foetuses frequently occur, and continue to live. This is borne out by the fact that, in the majority of these twin calves, the blood-forming – or haemopoetic – tissue is of mixed (chimeric or mosaic) genetic origin.

It is believed that under very exceptional conditions such mixed blood cells can occur in human beings also (in one fraternal twin out of, say, ten thousand). In fact one such case has been reported – that of the twenty-five-year-old Mrs. McK., who was found to contain a mixture of two genetically different types of red blood corpuscle.

Mr. McK. owed this peculiarity – which took geneticists by surprise – to the fact that she had shared her mother's womb with a male twin (who had died at the age of three months and of whose existence she was unaware until the laboratory test revealed the strange composition of her blood). She herself was group O, but her twin had been group A, and his haemopoetic cells, spontaneously grafted in the embryonic state, continued to produce A corpuscles twenty-five years later.

Needless to say, exchanges of embryonic tissue must occur even more frequently between identical twins, where, however, they cannot be detected since the two subjects are genetically identical.

As Medawar[2] pointed out, chimeras are some of nature's most remarkable products. In fact, Medawar's classic experiments on graft tolerance in embryos were first suggested by 'the natural experiment' of chimeric calves.

Clearly, advances in grafting-techniques will produce an ever-growing number of such human chimeras. We realize that this may have serious repercussions on our classical notions of man's individuality, but we feel that this is not the place to discuss them.

.   .   .   .   .

In this connexion, it must be mentioned that grafting is not the only cause of chimeras, since genetic mutations during embryonic development may give rise to organs of a different composition to the rest of the body. This phenomenon of somatic mutation is fairly common in animals and particularly in insects where individuals may combine male and female or different racial characteristics.

Such abnormalities have also been observed in birds. Dr. Tissot recently mentioned the case of a cock (reared by Greenwood in Edinburgh) whose right side was Sussex and whose left Rhode Island, as if some facetious conjurer had stuck the two halves together. The ludicrous appearance was heightened by the fact that, while the right half of the beak and the right foot were white (Sussex), the left half of the beak and the left foot were yellow (Rhode Island).

This cock was a cross between a Sussex and a Rhode Island, the two strains having divided out in the offspring.

Perhaps the case of different-coloured eyes falls into the same category. It has been said of Jan Clark, the film actress – 'the girl with the odd eyes '– that she inherited her brown eye from her German mother and her blue eye from her Swiss father, an explanation that is not genetically unacceptable. You might, if you wish, call Jan Clark a 'singular woman'.

Effeminate Men and Masculine Women
Some further peculiarities of our species can be found in the sexual sphere. To begin with, there is the typical case of the dichotomy between the somatic and the genetic sexuality. K. J. Moore and M. L. Barr's remarkable experiments – first on cats and then on other vertebrates including man – have shown an unsuspected sexual difference in the appearance of the cellular nucleus: female cells, suitably fixed and stained, reveal a small spot of chromatine close to the internal surface of the nuclear membrane. This spot, which is a veritable secondary sexual characteristic on the microscopic scale, is quite distinct from the chromosome disparity between the two sexes, which is very much more difficult to demonstrate.

Thanks to this distinctive characteristic, we can tell whether a given cell is derived from a male or from a female, no matter if the cell is taken from the blood, the skin, from scrapings of the mouth or the vagina, from the roots of the hair, or from bones or teeth. Furthermore, physicians have long been familiar with the so-called Turner-Albright syndrome (ovarian agenesis) characterized by impuberty and smallness of waist. Formerly these symptoms were attributed to early damage to the ovaries, and the subject was quite naturally taken to be genetically female. Now the examination of their cellular nuclei by the Moore and Barr technique has shown that practically all these subjects happen to be male.

From Jost's experiments with rabbits (the results of which can be applied to other mammals including man), we know that whenever a very young male embryo is castrated, it will present feminine characteristics. 'The embryonic testicle makes the male,' Jost declared. Thus it is extremely likely that the Turner-Albright syndrome is the result of a natural experiment in castration, during which the male gonad is prevented from secreting its hormones, thus producing the feminine appearance of the subject.

In this connexion, we must also mention the Pettersson-Bonnier syndrome which causes male subjects with undescended and generally sterile testicles to have the appearance, instincts, taste and temperament of women. This syndrome is hereditary and in many families it is transmitted through normal females. A number of hypotheses have been put forward to explain this phenomenon, and in particular it has been suggested that these intersexes may be the result of the presence of a third stock of chromosomes (triploidy). Beatty (who is the leading authority on polyploidy in mammals), while not completely dismissing this hypothesis, prefers to think of intersexes as sex-reversed men whose XY chromosome constitution had undergone a precocious change. The Barr test will undoubtedly help to resolve the problem whether these intersexes are in fact biologically 'peculiar'.

Other human intersexes occur in genetically female subjects (chromosome formula XX). Here the early sex reversal is often the result of an excess of suprarenal hormones, the effects of which are in some respects comparable to those of male hormones. They are often the results of benign tumours, and when such tumours occur in the embryo, the transformation of a female into a male is almost complete. If they occur at a later stage, the results may be such superficial signs of virility as, for instance, are found in bearded women. Sometimes such 'singular women' have been officially registered as boys.

Kitty Ponse mentions the case of one such person who contracted a marriage with another woman. Her glandular feminity was only revealed at autopsy. More extraordinary still, is the case recorded by Drs. Constantini and Toreilles (1942), recalled by Etienne Wolff in his Les Changements de sexe. Here, a twenty-five-year-old subject had male genitals, though with only one testicle on the left side. He had no beard, his limbs were rounded and his hips prominent.

When a laparotomy was performed to investigate severe abdominal pain, it was discovered that the right side contained a set of female sex organs: uterus, Fallopian tubes and one ovary. Both the female and the male organs were in functioning order, the ovary showing unmistakable signs of ovulation and the testicle containing fully developed spermatozoa that could be drawn off.

The subject was thus a simultaneous source of viable ova and sperms. Theoretically, at least, he could have been both father and mother. According to genetic laws, had self-fertilization been possible in his case (as it was in that of Witschi's hermaphrodite frogs), all the children would have been girls.

. . . . .

Now for a few words about a phenomenon that sometimes makes the headlines: adult women turning into men, and *vice versa*.

People veering from masculinity to femininity or from femininity to masculinity are certainly singular, even though their transformation often involves plastic surgery or hormonal therapy. The reader will remember the story of Robert Cowell, the brilliant aviator and the father of two daughters, who subsequently turned into a woman. If he was genetically female, i.e. having the sex chromosome constitution XX, he was, of course, bound to have had female offspring only. Still, his case was shrouded in too much mystery for us to express an opinion whether it does, in fact, resemble the results artificially produced in frogs and newts.

Female Lines of Descent

Another well-known human singularity is the family with disproportionate number of children of one particular sex.

We know that in man sex is generally determined by the existence of two genetic classes of sperms: those with X chromosomes producing girls and those with Y chromosomes producing boys. Since both types are represented in equal number, the sexes are evenly distributed throughout the world.

Now in certain human lines of descent there is a complete absence of one of the sexes, e.g. in the well-known case of the family in Nancy (reported by Lienhart and Vermelin) to whom not a single boy was born for three generations. Madame B's grandparents had six daughters, all of whom gave birth exclusively to daughters (8, 2, 2, 4, 2, and 9 respectively) – a grand total of thirty-three daughters in two generations. The third generation was also composed entirely of (39) girls. Hence the three generations produced seventy-two girls in seventy-two births.

While it is practically impossible to attribute all this to pure chance, it seems difficult to reconcile the existence of this feminiparous tendency in mothers with what we know of the father's role in sex determination. Is the explanation to be sought in the ova's affinity for spermatozoa with X chromosomes (an absolutely wild assumption since not a single case of such selective fertilization is known), in the fact that certain uterine secretions are toxic for spermatozoa with Y chromosomes, or finally in the fact that the humoral state during gestation is hostile to male foetuses? In any case, it seems likely that this feminiparous tendency is transmitted from mother to daughter in the cytoplasm of the ovule – a typical example of cytoplasmic transmission in the animal kingdom.[3]

A similarly disproportionate sex distribution was encountered by Harris when, in 1946, he investigated a family which, in ten generations, had produced only two girls in thirty-five births. Moreover, one of these girls was so much an inter-sex that there was some doubt whether she should even be registered a female. Nothing is known about the other girl, except that she died at the age of two.

These two singular families constitute 'natural experiments' that we still have difficulty in interpreting. It seems clear that if ever we should succeed in repeating nature's method, we shall have gone a long way towards solving the problem of voluntary sex determination.

Men with Multiple Sets of Chromosomes?

When discussing the Pettersson-Bonnier syndrome, we mentioned the assumption that this singularity might be the result of an additional set of chromosomes (polyploidy).

Natural polyploidy is not uncommon in amphibia (frogs, newts, etc.), where specimens have been found with cells containing three or even four sets of chromosomes instead of the normal pair. Natural polyploidy was also found in mice when Beatty and Fischberg made a study of ten-day-old embryos. Experimental polyploidy can easily be produced in amphibia, and it appears to have been induced in rabbits and pigs by Häggqvist and Bane after artificial insemination with chemically treated semen.

For the moment, there is no reliable evidence of polyploidy in man, though its existence must not be dismissed out of hand. Polyploidy in vertebrates is difficult to detect since it has no external symptoms of it, whereas, in invertebrates and plants, it is usually accompanied by gigantism. In any case, there can be little doubt that some women carry Y, i.e. male, chromosomes – in addition to their own XX chromosomes. These women are not distinguished by any sexual peculiarities, and their genetic singularity (XXY instead of XX) only becomes apparent from their irregular transmission of genes.

It is equally possible that there are men lacking in Y chromosomes, i.e. with the chromosome formula XO instead of the normal XY. This absence of the Y chromosome occurs in the vinegar fly where it is accompanied by sterility.

Fatherless Men

Strange though the questions may sound, it is permissible to ask whether human beings can be born in the absence of fertilization, just as happens when one out of ten thousand to a hundred thousand turkeys is hatched from a virgin egg.

Such virginally born creatures would indeed be the most singular of beings. It will be remembered that when Mrs. Haldane's article on this subject in the *Lancet* became the subject of a nation-wide inquiry by the *Sunday Pictorial*, a number of women wrote in to say that they had given birth in this way. One of them, Mrs. Emminarie Jones was examined by a panel of physicians and geneticists who concluded that, because of certain genetic peculiarities of mother and daughter, the claim could not be dismissed out of hand.

Beatty in his recent *Parthenogenesis and Polyploidy* in *Mammalian Development* (Cambridge, 1957), devotes an entire chapter to a discussion of the possibilities of spontaneous parthenogenesis in mammals. All his remarks apply equally well to man.

'Centuries of experiments' – Beatty writes – 'tell us that the young are not born of a mammal unless there has been a prior intervention of spermatozoa. . . . Yet we have seen examples of experimentally induced parthenogenesic development in mammalian embryos. These results give some encouragement for asking . . . "How would the animals be identified?"

'A little reflection shows that there are difficulties. The first and probably the most important is that the animal breeder is not expecting parthenogenesis. If an apparently uninseminated female mammal produces an offspring, the breeder is more likely to attribute the event to a misalliance, or to an error in the records. Further, a breeder would not be expected to publicize an inexplicable birth in pedigree stock. Similar considerations might weigh in breeding of laboratory animals. In man, unmarried mothers have sometimes claimed that no father was involved, but the validity of such claims is normally ignored.'

As Beatty observes, spontaneous parthenogenesis would be even more difficult to detect in married women. If the child is born at normal term, its singular origin would not even be suspected, and if the child is born out of term it might be described as an instance of superfoetation.

In the particular case of our species, parthenogenetic offspring would necessarily be female, though not necessarily a faithful replica of the mother – her younger twin, as it were. This is due to the fact that the 'parthenogenetic' ovule can double its chromosomes after first having undergone chromosome reduction.

Though complete parthenogenesis in man seems rather improbable, partial or rudimentary parthenogenesis does in fact occur in our species. Physicians are familiar with dermoid cysts of the ovary (up to 15 or 20 cysts have been found in a single gland). These cysts seem to have a hereditary or racial origin. In 1891, Mathias-Duval, and particularly his pupil Répin, put forward the thesis that these cysts were the results of an atypical development of a virgin ovule, a theory that is still held by many biologists, and by Vandel, Witschi and Mosinger, in particular.

Thus Witschi mentions Neumann's strange observation of an ovary, with two distinct cysts containing strands of dark and fair hair respectively. In this case, the mother – who must have been dark-haired – was thought to have carried a dark and a fair-hair gene, both of which were present in the cyst-producing ovule.

In such rudimentary parthenogenesis, Vandel saw 'an undeniable tendency (of the human ovule) to parthenogenetic development'. He thought it very likely, therefore, that human ovules could successfully be subjected to experimental parthenogenesis.[4]

Thousands of Embryos in one Tumour

In this quick survey of human singularities, we cannot ignore the memorable work of Albert Peyron, even though we still do not know whether his was a grain of folly or a grain of genius or – why not? – a bit of each.

Peyron claimed to have observed certain testicular teratomata (tumours of the testicle) in man containing hundreds of thousands of embryo-like structures. When Professor Limousin sent him the famous tumour No. 11,013, Peyron dissected it into thirty thousand slices, each of which showed a profusion of embryo-like structures. Peyron observed their resemblance to normal early primate embryos, and even distinguished their successive stages of morphological development: gastrulation, formation of the neurenteric canal, of the amniotic cavity, etc.

By means of this very strange 'experiment' nature has provided the embryologist with the means of studying those early stages in human development which are otherwise difficult to observe. Peyron even went so far as to consider the possibility of culturing these structures, thus producing sectionally-propagated human beings – a strange perspective for the future, this!

Where does this 'nursery' of embryos in the testicle spring from? Is it a form of spermal parthenogenesis complicated by polyembriony, both set off by, or related to, a testicular tumour? Peyron carefully distinguished these parthenogenetic and polyembryonic structures from parasitic embryoid bodies caused by foetal inclusions and resembling the case of double monstrosity. It is clearly to that category that we must attribute the case of male parthenogenesis reported by MM. Lombard, Ferrand, and Legenissel to the *Académie de Médecine* in 1953. Here, a four-month-old foetus was found in the abdomen of a twenty-month-old boy.

Though Peyron's discoveries were at first met with almost general scepticism, eminent biologists like M. Caullery and P. Wintrebert were quick to realize their importance. Since then, his work has been confirmed by a great many other leading biologists.[5] When J. A. Gaillard (1956) wrote that polyembryony was but one of many ways in which the embryonal bud can develop,[6] he did not detract from the merit of Peyron's magnificent work and from the value of his 'extraordinary publications'. Moreover, in his own work, Gaillard made use of Peyron's 'extraordinary' collection of testicular teratomata. 'Extraordinary' is the word that crops up in every discussion of the work of a man whose name is inseparably linked with the history of embryoids, and who has probably opened up an entirely new chapter in human biology.

In a fairly recent issue of the *Journal of Clinical Pathology*, R. Winston Evans discusses the presence of embryo-like structures in human teratoma testis.[7]

Evans noted the similarity of these small bodies to the early developmental stages of mammalian embryos and that they sometimes 'mimic' the form of normal early human embryos. He thinks that some light might be shed on their development by transplanting them on rats. I cannot hide my surprise at the absence of Peyron's name in the bibliography of Evans's paper.[8]

In any case, androgenesis or male parthenogenesis, is another of nature's strange experiments revealing, as it does, the unsuspected potentialities of the male germinal tissue. If we should ever manage to discover the nature of the different factors producing this phenomenon, we are sure to find that there will be important consequences in experimental embryology.

A Variant of Parthenogenesis

A curious variant of parthenogenesis – gynogenesis – could well be called parthenogenesis through the sperm. Sometimes – both under natural and experimental conditions – a sperm will become completely inactive once it has entered the ovum. This need not impede the ovum's development but, of course, the offspring will be devoid of paternal chromosomes.

Gynogenesis may occur when the sperm has been submitted to radiation or to chemical poisons, or even when it belongs to a different species from that of the ovum. In that case gynogenesis is tantamount to pseudo-hybridization. Gynogenesis in man was discussed as long ago as 1910, when the great French biologist Yves Delage attributed its occurrence to the presence of sperms that had become impaired through alcohol, morphine, cocaine, nicotine, or syphilis.[9]

Delage concluded his paper by saying: 'It is not impossible that we might meet parthenogenetic individuals in the street without ever suspecting their most singular origin. This happens because that singularity is not betrayed by any obvious signs. . . .

'Only by the careful observation of susceptible subjects can we hope to form a final opinion on this subject. This work ought to be of great interest to biologists, though it is medical practitioners who have looked after a family for a number of generations and who know the nosological history of all its members, who are particularly qualified to carry it out.'

Delage also envisaged the possibility of parthenogenesis due to defective pairing, alluding discreetly 'to the very exceptional but nevertheless established fact of sexual intercourse between human beings of either sex and animals'.

This same suggestion was recently made by L. Bounoure as a possible explanation for the birth in 1897 of an anencephalic (headless) monster. The monster's mother was a sixteen-year-old girl who shared a caravan near Vichy with her father and a monkey. She had had no contact with the outside world, and malicious rumour had it that the girl was having incestuous relations with her father.

Bounoure[10] prefers to think that the monster was the

result of sexual intercourse between the girl and the monkey, though I must confess that, in this case, incest strikes me as a far less unlikely explanation.

.   .   .   .   .

We have just examined a number of 'natural experiments', some undoubtedly authentic, some less trustworthy. Amongst the latter, I would include the alleged existence of telegony. Certain breeders and even certain doctors think that, because of an effect of a previous sire, a dam can, by a second sire, produce progeny resembling the first. Thus a European woman married to a negro could remarry a European and give birth to a coloured child.

Some biologists have recently tried to explain this 'phenomenon' by assuming that the D.N.A. (desoxyribonucleic acid) of the first sire's sperms has had a modifying effect on the dam's ovules. This would be nature's way of producing in man what Benoit achieved experimentally in his ducks.

While I myself think that telegony is just a myth, it is only fair to add that so eminent a naturalist as Alfred Giard believed in it firmly enough to write:

'The direct action of the first male on subsequent progeny is a fact whose sociological consequences have not been sufficiently noted. To some extent [these consequences] would justify the seignorial rights which noblemen of old arrogated to themselves on their subjects' bridal night. At a time, when the nobility took foremost place on the social scale, the exercise of that right might well have helped to improve the race. Children born under that influence, might have played just as great a role as bastards in raising the standard of the lower classes and in preparing the emancipation of 1789.'[11]

How odd to hear telegony used as a justification of the *jus primae noctis*, and to find it cited as one of the factors of the French Revolution!

We could add to our list of man's alleged peculiarities by mentioning the growing of a third set of teeth, quoted by Erasmus Darwin, Sigaud de la Fond, and even by the sceptical Fontenelle, but we must end here, and see what conclusions we have reached.

We have mentioned very briefly that some of nature's 'experiments' such as polyembryony, the Turner-Albright syndrome, and dermoidal cysts, have already thrown much light on human biology. Other phenomena, such as androgenesis in testicular tumours, and the disproportionate propagation of one particular sex are not yet fully understood, but may well tell us a great deal in the future.

These experiments of nature are particularly valuable, since we cannot perform analogous laboratory experiments on man. But even our study of zoology and botany can also benefit greatly from, for instance, such natural experiments as the parasitic castration in insects, the feminization of crabs under the action of sacculine, the existence of intersexes in *Drosophila*, the masculinization of old hens and old hen-pheasants, spontaneous sex transformations in amphibians and birds, the fusion of eggs in *Ascaris*, the existence of freemartins (imperfect females of the ox kind, twin-born with a male) whose sex glands are masculinized by the male twin *in utero*, etc.

While certain experiments of nature can only be interpreted by laboratory experiments, the reverse is equally true. Occasionally, though ignorant of the means nature employs, we can imitate her processes, e.g. in the case of polyembryony. On other occasions, we cannot copy her, no matter what procedure we use. This is the case with freemartinism which we cannot reproduce experimentally despite all recent advances in hormone, and particularly sex hormone, chemistry. Hormone treatment does, in fact, produce modifications of the secondary sexual characteristics of the mammalian foetus, but no matter what dosage is given or at what stage of embryonic development, the structural alterations of the female gland found in freemartinism cannot be achieved experimentally.

We have mentioned the effect of natural on laboratory experiments. Thus the phenomenon of parasitic castration has suggested research on the sexual hormones of the invertebrates; the existence of chimeras in *Drosophila* has suggested experiments on pigmentation hormones; the discovery that the blood of most dizygotic cattle twins is partially chimeric has suggested experiments on the tolerance of embryos with respect to grafting. On the other hand, laboratory experiments have often caused scientists to look for natural experiments, whose existence is suspected the moment their possibility has been appreciated.

A whole methodological treatise on the relationship between natural and laboratory experiments could be written. Francis Bacon was one of the first to foresee, and to note, the importance of 'deviating instances', i.e. errors of nature, 'things which are vague and monstrous' wherein nature reveals herself to us unbidden by 'declining and deflecting from her ordinary course'.

'Nor must we desist from inquiry with regard to them until the cause of this declension is discovered. . . . For he who knows the ways of nature will more easily observe her deviations also; and again he who knows her deviations will more accurately describe her ways.'

And Bacon added that we must make 'a collection or particular natural history of all prodigies and monstrous births of Nature, of everything, in short, that is new, rare and unusual in Nature. But this must be accompanied by a most rigid scrutiny, that confidence may be established. . . . These [witnesses] must be drawn from grave and trustworthy history, and from true reports.'

It is my sincere hope that, in these pages, I have heeded that advice.

REFERENCES

[1] Newly born babies, injected with paternal leucocytes at birth, were given small skin grafts from the father when they were six months old. After seven weeks of observation, these grafts were still living (Woodruff, *Transplant. Bull.*, U.S.A., 1957).

[2] Medawar: *The Uniqueness of the Individual*, London, Methuen, 1957.

[3] In certain flies (*Drosophila willistoni*) some lines produce a large preponderance of female progeny; this peculiar sex distribution is pathological and is probably caused by a virus (Malaglowkin and Poulson *Science*, 1957).

[4] A. Vandel: *La Parthenogenese*, Doin, 1930, p. 278.

[5] *See* René Dufau's: *Les Tumeurs du Testicule et les syndromes de masculinisation*, Lefrançois, 1941.

[6] *Histogenèse des dysembryomes testiculaires. Les images initiales et les aspects évolutifs*, Bulletin de l'Association française pour l'étude du Cancer, vol. 43, 1956.

[7] *Developmental Stages of Embryo-like Bodies in Teratoma Testis*, J. of Cl. Path. (1957), 10, 31.

[8] L. C. Simard discovered microscopic structures recalling the first stages of human embryo development in an ovarian tumour. This would probably be another instance of parthenogenesis-cum-polyembryony (*Cancer*, 1957).

[9] *La parthénogenese peut-elle exister dans l'espèce humaine?* Biologia, May 1913.

[10] *Semaine des Hôpitaux*, May 1957.

[11] Giard: *Controverses transformistes*, 1903.

4

Biology and Maladjustment

I N this essay we shall discuss the influence of biological factors on human conduct and particularly on the conduct of maladjusted children and adolescents.

A child is called maladjusted when, because of physical or mental aberrations, it has become incapable of adapting to the rules of normal life without special medical, education or social steps. It is believed that in France alone, there are about 500,000 such cases, and their existence clearly poses very grave social and educational problems, particularly since many of these maladjusted children are quite unfit to live any kind of normal life and often tend towards delinquency.

While most physical aberrations can be shown to spring from biological causes, it is difficult to define the role of biology in psychological or character deficiencies. Two factors go into the making of man – or, for that matter, of all living beings: internal (hereditary or genetic) factors and external (environmental) factors. While the hereditary factors are necessarily biological, the environmental factors can be biological as well as psychological or social.

To investigate this problem fully, therefore, we must first examine all the hereditary factors and then all the environmental factors which can affect man's biological structure at any stage of his development.

Let us begin by recalling some basic facts.

A child is the result of a joint contribution by his parents, each of whom supplies a cell, a minute speck of protoplasm from the colony of cells that constitutes their bodies. When the father's sperm penetrates and fertilizes the mother's ovule, the ovule becomes an ovum. The ovum travels to the womb, in whose wall it develops into an embryo, a foetus, and finally into a baby.

Thus, the parents' microscopic contributions form the very tenuous bridge from one generation to the next, and determine the child's entire heritage. Moreover, we know that this inheritance is carried in only the *nucleus* of each germ cell, i.e. in the somewhat denser region of the cell containing the chromosomes. Each parental nucleus contains the same number of chromosomes (24), and hence it is obvious that each of the two progenitors makes an equal contribution to the child's biological heritage.

This is not the place for giving even a summary description of the mechanics of heredity. Suffice it to say, that the chromosomes themselves are made up of a number of even smaller particles, the genes, and that every nucleus contains tens of thousands of genes, each of which play a distinct role. Moreover, genes can exist in different states, each state conferring different properties upon them.[1]

According to its state (or its chemical composition), a given gene will determine eye coloration, hair colour or texture, the shape of the nose, the blood group, etc. Different genes can combine in every possible way to produce all the striking differences between individuals that we observe in daily life.

For simplicity, let us suppose that man were a species with only two different sets of genes producing respectively brown or blue eyes and dark or fair hair. Their combination could result in four distinct individuals, viz. individuals with brown eyes and dark hair, individuals with brown eyes and fair hair, individuals with blue eyes and dark hair, and finally individuals with blue eyes and fair hair.

Let us now postulate an additional set of genes producing coarse or fine hair; the three sets together could produce eight different individuals, viz. individuals with brown eyes, dark and fine hair, individuals with brown eyes, dark and coarse hair, individuals with brown eyes, fair and fine hair, individuals with brown eyes, fair and coarse hair, etc.

We shall not bother the reader with a list of all possible combinations, but shall simply state that n sets of genes can give rise to $2n$ combinations and hence to 2^n types of individuals. Since thousands of sets of genes exist in the human species, the number of possible combinations is quite astronomical. By applying the formula, we can show that any union can, potentially, produce millions of millions of combinations, a number far exceeding the world's actual population. It follows that there is very little, if any, chance that genes would combine in such a way as to produce two identical individuals. In the lottery of birth the same number is never drawn twice. Hence every human being starts with a genetic inheritance that is strictly his alone and that stamps his biological individuality – his uniqueness – right from the start of his life.

Man's essential originality is due to a unique association of common elements, just as all symphonies consist of the combination of only a few notes and all literary master-pieces of only a few letters. Mankind's individual possibilities are so great that even were our species to exist for another billion years, no one individual need ever be duplicated, and it goes without saying that this uniqueness plays a paramount role in man's relations with his environment.

'The profound sorrow we experience on the death of a friend,' Schopenhauer wrote, 'is due to our feeling that each individual possesses something indefinable that is his alone, and hence absolutely irreplaceable. *Omne individuum irreparibile. . . .*'

This notion of biological uniqueness is felt intuitively by every man. No man has a true counterpart, though he may have an identical twin resembling him in every morphological and physiological detail. But even this exception simply proves the rule: identical twins are never the chance results of two separate unions; derived from the same ovum, they result from the same combination of genes.

The fact that two individuals may be as like as two peas, merely serves to emphasize our own uniqueness. If twins have so often captured the imagination of poets and particularly of dramatists – from Antiphanes, Aristophanes, Xenarchus, Alexis of Thurium, Menander, through Plautus's Menaechni right up to Jean Anouilh in our own time – I think this is not so much due to the fact that the twin theme lends itself so well to comic situations of mistaken identity, as to the dramatic *dénouement* disclosing the real – and unique – individuality of each of the pair.

Now that we have taken stock of man's uniqueness, we may well ask if certain combinations of genes are hallmarked for producing maladjusted individuals, or at least individuals who have difficulty in adapting themselves to their environment. As regards physical shortcomings the answer is quite clear: congenital blindness, deafness, bone and muscular deficiencies, and many other abnormalities such as haemophilia . . . all cause grave adaptation problems. Similarly, a great many mental deficiencies are known to be congenital, to have been 'imprinted' upon the genes. Phenylpyruvic oligophrenia is a typical example of this type of mental deficiency. It is transmitted by a recessive gene, i.e. it can only be produced when both parents carry that gene, albeit in its latent form.

Phenylpyruvic oligophrenia could be called 'chemical idiocy', since the presence of phenylpyruvic acid (a chemical substance which results from an error in metabolism) in the urine is the main criterion in the diagnosis of this disease. Fortunately phenylpyruvic oligophrenia is very rare, its incidence being of the order of one in twenty-five to fifty million of the population.

Many other types of idiocy and mental deficiency caused by degeneration of nerve tissue are also congenital, e.g. juvenile amaurotic idiocy (also produced by a recessive gene), Wilson's disease, progressive lenticular degeneration, cerebral atrophy, congenital cerebral ataxia, Friedreich's ataxia, neurofibromatosis, and Huntington's chorea. Though less obvious, the role of heredity is also undeniable in cyclothymia, in schizophrenia and in certain forms of epilepsy. Over and above these manifest conditions, fortunately rare, there are a great many diseases and deficiencies in which the genetic factor, though not decisive, tends to weight the balance on the wrong side.

The reader will appreciate that individuals whose genetic endowment renders them less adaptable in some situations need not necessarily be maladjusted in others. Hereditary factors which assure perfect adaptation in all circumstances are probably as rare as hereditary factors producing complete maladjustment.

This brings us to the formidable problem of the hereditary

transmission of mental faculties, and of character and instinctual traits. Though some have claimed that intelligence, will-power, attentiveness, endurance, perversity, aggressiveness and timidity, skill and clumsiness, cruelty and irritability, are handed down directly from father to son, I myself am very sceptical of this assertion. True, there can be no doubt that different individuals inherit different intellectual and emotional capacities, but that is as far as we can go. It seems only logical that genetic specificity should lead to psychological specificity just as it leads to physical specificity. This is also born out by the fact that, in dogs or rats for instance, we can selectively breed strains differing in behaviour, and last but not least by the study of identical twins which has shown that individuals with the same hereditary factors are psychologically akin. The psychological resemblance between parent and child, which is often cited as further evidence for the hereditary transmission of psychological traits, strikes me as inadmissible evidence since here it is difficult to distinguish heredity from imitation of the parent or from the influence of the home.

A point closely connected with our subject, is the *correlation* between certain psychological, hereditary and physical traits. Mme Léone Bourdel has suggested that each blood group is associated with a certain type of behaviour, and that significant statistical differences would be discovered if the distribution of blood groups in the professional classes were investigated.

Others have tried to correlate body type (asthenic, athletic, pyknic) with temperament (schizoid, cycloid), or to correlate constitutional factors with extrovert and introvert behaviour. While the whole thing strikes me as somewhat vague and dubious, there is unquestionably some connexion between physiology and psychology, if only because of the effects of coenesthesia (i.e. the total mass of sensations derived from the internal organs), or even as a result of seeing ourselves in the mirror. Clearly, our temperament would be affected by what the glass reveals: tallness or shortness, strength or weakness, beauty or ugliness. In brief, there seems to be little doubt that genetic differences are partly responsible for man's mental and behavioural differences. Professor Heuyer, the famous child psychiatrist, put it as follows: 'When we carefully collect all the data on a child's heredity for at least two generations, together with all the data on its home and social environment, we can no longer be satisfied with the theory of constitutional morbidity, with the psychoanalytical theory of environmental pressure, or with political and economic explanations. On perusing the data, we must conclude that the emotional climate of the child's home and school environment have a direct effect on his conduct, that poor social conditions and poverty facilitate psychopathological and antisocial reactions, but that, all things being equal, two ordinary children brought up under the same conditions and in the same home will behave differently while two monozygotic twins will behave in an appreciably similar fashion. The role of heredity is undeniable.'[2]

.   .   .   .   .

Since children are born with distinct psychological capacities, which render them more or less adaptable to a given environment, we might well ask if the parents' way of life can affect their children's inheritance. This is the hotly

contested problem of the transmission of acquired characters. If its proponents are correct, those parents who live a
normal life, who acquire the correct social responses, who
adapt correctly to their environment, have a better
chance of producing adjusted children than parents who
are badly adapted.

While I do not wish to discuss all the pros and cons of
this argument, I may be permitted to point out that the
biological findings in the matter are quite clear: the parents'
behaviour – good or bad – has no effects whatsoever on
the genes they transmit to their children. True, a parent may
transmit those psychological traits favouring or opposing
adaptation that he himself has inherited, but he can never
transmit the method whereby he has utilized his own genetic
gifts or handicaps. It might be argued that, even so, the
effects of parental alcoholism seem to be one of the
causes of mental aberration, character disorders and delinquency.

Here it is important to make a distinction: the direct
action of alcoholism on the germ cells is questioned by a
great many specialists; the mere fact that Elderton and
Pearson (1910) were able to maintain that the descendants
of alcoholics are often superior to the children of total
abstainers, shows that the problem is by no means as straightforward as some would claim.

On the other hand, it must be remembered that the
alcoholic – the true alcoholic – is generally a psychopath
and an anxiety neurotic. If his own mental aberration is
hereditary, he may, of course, transmit it to his own descendants. Quite apart from that, however, paternal alcoholism by affecting the smooth course of pregnancy, and the
children's early home life, may have serious repercussions

on the child's future. Worse still, maternal alcoholism may directly affect the development of the foetus through the bloodstream, or of the nurseling through the mother's milk.

This has brought the discussion round to the mother's biological influence, so much more important than that of the father, whose almost instantaneous biological role is restricted to contributing his genes to the child.

Let us look at the fertilized ovum, i.e. the human being in the unicellular stage. Even at this early stage man, by virtue of his genetic heritage, is already a perfectly distinct individual. Human inequality begins at the moment of conception; already in this tiny speck of protoplasm which is the ovum, the seeds of happiness and unhappiness have been planted. Thereafter pure genetic determinism will be tempered more and more by environmental factors.

Now the child's earliest environment is obviously the mother's womb, with which the embryo, and later the foetus, will rest in intimate connexion for the nine months of gestation. Here, again, the child may be affected by different influences, for, contrary to what I myself have written, all wombs are not identical.

There is the question of the mother's age.[3] We know that the incidence of *mongolism* which is one of the causes of mental deficiency (according to Shuttleworth about 5 per cent of all the feeble-minded are mongolian idiots), is much greater in children with relatively older mothers (from thirty-eight years onwards). In addition, mongolian idiocy is a congenital deficiency – here we have a classic example of the inter-action of hereditary and environmental factors.

We have already mentioned some effects of maternal

alcoholism on the foetus and the child. Equally harmful effects can be produced by other intoxicants or drugs: nicotine, morphine, noxious fumes, the ever-increasing habit of taking tranquillizers such as phenobarbitone, phenergan, and largactil. X-rays may also affect the foetus, producing certain types of leukaemia and possibly certain changes in the nervous system.

Other maternal factors which may damage the foetus are toxaemia of pregnancy, diabetes, cardiac and circulatory insufficiencies (which cause the blood to become deficient in oxygen); the excessive secretion of such hormones as cortisone; malnutrition and mechanical compression due to tightness of the amnion.

Special mention must be made of the role of viruses. From the remarkable work of the Australian ophthalmologist Gregg we know that German measles, that relatively mild infection, may cause abnormalities of the foetus's heart, ears and eyes, if it is contracted by the mother during the first two months of pregnancy. Other virus and spirochaetal infections (syphilis) can cause nervous lesions.[4]

Finally, the mother's psychological attitude may also have an appreciable effect on the foetus. Her mood is communicated by way of the sympathetic system to the foetus's humoral environment depriving it of, or enriching it with, certain hormones or special substances such as the recently discovered serotonine.

In the last few years, various psychiatrists and particularly Phyliss Greenacre, and Françoise Dolto, have stressed the effects of the mother's mood on the foetus. This is far from being a return to the old wives' tale that a mother's 'bad thoughts' can cause her child to have spots or birthmarks or to the recent claim made by, I forget which glossy paper, that the mother's memories become inscribed on the brain of the foetus. What it does mean is that there is an increasing conviction that 'repeated maternal stimuli can set up and maintain a state of irritability and hyper-activity which, together with constitutional factors, can engender a certain typology.'[5] Thus, a child can be born anxious or at least predisposed to anxiety or to spasmo-philia, when its mother refuses to come to terms with her pregnancy or when she has had conjugal or other difficulties during that period.

Finally, there may be blood incompatibilities between mother and foetus. If the mother is Rhesus negative and the foetus Rhesus positive, Rhesus antibodies may develop, pass into the foetal circulation and cause haemolysis. Fourteen per cent of all cases of infantile encephalopathies are due to blood incompatibility, and Heuyer thinks that less disabilities may also result from the same cause.

．　　　．　　　．　　　．　　　．

The moment a child is born, it faces a new set of risks.

Even if the confinement was normal, the child may have had traumatic shocks due to prolonged labour, the use of forceps, or to the twisting of the cord. Also, the first breath taken by the new-born child is due to the effect of a slight, or sometimes definite, asphyxia resulting from the separation of the placenta. Maternal syphilis and the consequent vascular lesions predispose the child to obstetric traumata.

Little's disease is commonly attributed to obstetric conditions, and the same must be true of many cases of cerebral lesions which only become manifest during subsequent infectious diseases.

.　　　.　　　.　　　.　　　.

At last the child lies in its cot. It has a hard past behind it; a long history full of incidents. The child might well be called a biological case-book. Even if its genetic heritage has left no stigmata, even if its pre-natal adventure and its birth have left the child unscathed – it has already been subject to a host of influences affecting its future life and adaptability, for better or for worse.

The nurseling, as Arnold Gesell has shown, is an individual whose psychological personality is expressed by his mood, responsiveness, sociability, sensitivity, patience, facial expression, self-confidence, agility and attentiveness. Even at this early stage it is extremely difficult, if not utterly impossible, to distinguish between the nurseling's hereditary and acquired traits, because – and this cannot be stressed enough – the baby's personality has already been moulded by a great many environmental factors. We have seen that these factors will play an ever-increasing role as breast feeding, weaning, child diseases, teething troubles, etc., run their inevitable course.

The child's biological structure may now be directly affected by such nervous diseases as encephalitis, by glandular upsets particularly of the thyroid and the hypophysis, by hepatitis, diabetes, etc. In many cases, neuropathological hereditary traits aggravate the psychological consequences of organic afflictions.

Nor can early psychological influences be ignored. Spitz has shown the effects of maternal love on the earliest stages of the child's life, and Freudians have stressed and analysed the subsequent influences of the family environment. While I do not wish to minimize the value of the psycho-analytical contribution – I attach great importance to Freud's teachings and believe that they are not yet sufficiently applied and appreciated, at least in France – it would be a crude error to oppose psycho-analysis to the convincing evidence of biology and organic pathology. The connexion and interrelation between biology and psychology cannot be emphasized too strongly.

No doubt frustrations, childhood conflicts, fraternal jealousy and the attitude of the parents, play a capital role in the genesis of maladjusted behaviour. However, these psychological influences are tempered by the child's hereditary constitution, and, conversely, the biological structure is modified by these psychological factors. Thus it becomes impossible to separate the psychological event from the biological events that invariably precede and follow it.

Freud himself never mistook the role of constitutional factors in the fate of the libido and in the genesis of the neuroses. As N. Bouvet[6] said, 'Freud, who was first and foremost a neurologist, was nevertheless unable to build up a coherent neurological system which was not, in some way, connected with organic activities. According to Freud, hereditary constitutional factors may account for the fixation of various instinctual energies at a stage of development which would normally be surpassed. Thus a heightened congenital erogenous sensitivity of the anal zone can cause libidinal fixation on that zone in a way that is characteristic of the stage of development known as the anal stage.' The same point of view is held by Federn and by Anna Freud who is so faithfully continuing her father's great work.

Françoise Dolto made the shrewd observation that children of the 'sensation type' suffer more from maternal frustration than children of the 'abstract type'.[7] According to Heuyer, children with even mild attacks of encephalitis may have a heightened susceptibility to subsequent traumatic affect blocks.

There can be little doubt that hereditary or innate biological factors affect man's psychological vigour and resistance to stress and perhaps the intensity and quality of his instinctual drives also. We can thus assert that biological factors insinuate themselves into every aspect of man's life, even where they are least suspected.

Now let us look at the other side of the coin: the effects of psychology on biology. Spitz's careful observations have shown that young children deprived of their mother (or of a mother substitute) become morally and psychologically stunted, so much so that they have growing troubles and a greatly lowered resistance to infections. Furthermore, psycho-analysis and psycho-somatic medicine have made it clear that anxiety can lead to organic symptoms and even to lesions (ulcers, cavities in the lung, etc.).

The interaction of physical and psychological factors is clearly brought out in the following brief case histories: A fifteen-year-old boy, who suffered from a congenital impairment of vision, became a confirmed thief. His repeated acts of petty larceny were found to be connected with his visual troubles. The boy would have been cured of his mental abnormality by a frank acceptance of his organic disability (case cited by Langeveld, 1954). Can we say that the physical abnormality was the direct cause of

[136]

the mental abnormality? Clearly, not all children with his complaint would have reacted in his particular way. No doubt, this boy's psychological difficulties were accentuated by congenital factors.

Another child, who contracted poliomyelitis, became neurotically cruel to the point of trying to injure other children by throwing stones at them. Clearly, poliomyelitis is not in itself an adequate explanation of his maladjustment. Psychological, constitutional and environmental factors must have played their part also, let alone the possibility of an hereditary susceptibility to poliomyelitis.

A third child, morbidly introspective as the result of his repeated scholastic failures, spent two years in a sanatorium with tuberculosis. In the end he ran away and attempted suicide. What is our verdict? Was his maladjustment due to lack of parental affection, to hereditary traits that made him incapable of dealing with difficult situations, to early morbidity, to defective intelligence, or to tuberculosis (which might have been the result of his poor constitution or his psychological weakness)?

We could go on endlessly citing similar examples to illustrate the interaction of congenital and acquired, and of organic and psychological factors, or the relation between the organic consequences of the latter and the psychological consequences of the former, between heredity and conduct, and the influence of conduct on the expression of hereditary traits.

In many cases of maladjustment, a careful analysis would reveal a tangled skein of causes, an accumulation of effects, any one of which may well have sufficed for producing lack of adaptation. The problem is beset by a host of 'ifs' – some futile, some legitimate: if this child had not

[137]

inherited such genes, if that mother had been more careful, if the confinement had been easier, if the child had not contracted a disease at an early age, if it had had a different home, if it had not been the only child, if it could have sublimated a given instinctual tendency and turned it to good effect instead of harming society. . . .

Nor does this exhaust the possibilities. Some children might have adjusted to life in the country but cannot adjust to life in the city, others might have become adjusted to an intellectual life but cannot adjust to the life of a manual labourer and *vice versa*.

In general, it is true to say that bad economic conditions often aggravate a child's lack of adaptation. How many maladjusted people would not have been able to live a normal life had they been born to better circumstances, blessed with care and attention, a good education, and stricter parental control! Material difficulties, at least, would have been spared them, and hence the detrimental, and sometimes the perverting, effects of deprivation and misery would not have been added to their emotional and moral difficulties. There is no need to adduce further evidence, since in a society like ours which according to Charles Richet 'bestows everything on the foetus of the rich', inequality of circumstance and of education, and their brutal consequences on the individual, are too obvious to merit discussion.

Everyone knows that delinquency – so often a consequence of maladjustment – is much more widespread in the lower classes – 80 per cent of delinquents come from poor families. No wonder then, that Heuyer could write that 'the causes of juvenile delinquency are social and not moral'. Renan realized this when he said long ago:

'What kind of chance is it, I ask you, that all criminals stem from the same class?' Strange though it may sound, it is true to say that social classes differ not only in their life expectancy but also in their crime expectancy!

An individual's social origins may be the deciding factors in turning maladjustment into delinquency. Thus while a maladjusted child born in a hovel may turn into a danger-ous criminal, born into a good home it might merely have turned into one of those good-for-nothing playboys who haunt the bars and the casinos.

Of course, delinquency exists in the upper classes also, albeit under a different guise: lack of scruples and sharp practice under the protection of the Law. In the eyes of the psychologist these men are more akin to burglars than to respectable tradesmen.

Finally, in this rapid and necessarily incomplete sum-mary of the causes of maladjustment, we cannot ignore those special demoralizing factors which, though perhaps charac-teristic of all ages, are certainly characteristic of ours. I cannot resist citing M. Brauner's words:

'In the street, our children are the daily witnesses of every kind of human degradation and depravity. The placards call them to a way of life where success means shouting above everyone else and treading on other peoples' toes. . . . Newsvendors purvey journals, allegedly written for children, full of horror, drawn knives, and pointed revolvers. . . . Adult papers are in no way different. Their headlines, too, scream with murder and the child cannot help seeing sensational reports on the stalls or on the family table. . . . Half-dressed women adorn the paper's every page and are bound to arouse precocious curiosities that must ultimately impede the child's normal sexual

[139]

education. Children are shown the wrecks of aeroplanes and the latest atomic weapons so that life must appear to them made for destroying what imaginative minds have created, and history as the constant invention of novelties. In the extravagances of a pin-up girl or of a multi-millionaire and in the latest dictates of absurd fashion, the child is made to discover the meaning of modern life.

'Reason enough for becoming maladjusted. . . .'

Reason enough, indeed! But even so, we can add, *ad nauseam*, to Brauner's harsh, though not unfair, list: universal insecurity due to the terrifying advances of nuclear science, loss of traditional certainty, the decline of absolutes, the destruction of all former values, the cheapness of human life, a general and all-embracing scepticism which seeks nothing but immediate pleasure, the march of automation, the fantastic acceleration of the rhythm of life, the platitudes of school broadcasts, the growth of public exhibitionism; complacency about the unhealthy, sordid and perverse to the point of preferring decadence to vigour; the bravado of the pornographer, the bad example set by men in high places; the weakness of a leadership whose bad conscience makes it fear strength – in brief the frailty of a civilization that has failed to endow its knowledge with meaning, its powers with limits, its freedom with an ideal. . . .

It would be wrong to assert categorically that maladjustment is becoming increasingly rife – psychologists may simply have improved their diagnoses, or else the ever-growing complexities of social life may have raised the required standard of adaptation. But if maladjustment had in fact grown in modern times there would be no shortage of reasons for this increase. Medical advances alone, by vitiating the effects of natural selection, and by aiding the survival of a host of individuals who would otherwise have died in infancy, must have contributed to a higher rate of physical and mental maladjustment.

Since the problem of maladjustment impinges upon juvenile – and even on adult – delinquency, we cannot ignore altogether the equivocal questions of moral responsibility and liberty. We have just listed – and by no means fully! – the main genetic physiological, pathological, psychological, and sociological causes of abnormal behaviour. We have seen how, in the genesis of maladjustment, hereditary factors co-operate with the environment, and how natural inequality is the handmaiden of human injustice.

The eighteenth-century philosopher Helvetius postulated the fundamental identity of all human beings, and their equal capacity for virtue since, he argued, 'how otherwise could Divine justice or even secular justice expect the same results from different machines? Would God have given all men the same Law without giving each of them the same means of obeying that Law?'[8]

No matter what our philosophic or religious convictions may be, I think no one can continue to entertain the idea that all men are equally capable of functioning for the common good. Nobody would deny that by virtue of their genes, their hormones, their nervous constitution, their early conditioning, some men have the greatest difficulty in behaving in a socially acceptable way.

This is what the great physiologist Robert Courrier had to say on the effects of hormones:[9] 'Psychological life can be largely influenced by hormones. . . . The known facts about cretinism, depression, agitation or torpor, asthenia or impulsive behaviour, leave no doubt of their hormonal origin – the effects of the thyroid, the suprarenal, the gonads and the pituitary are quite obvious. From American statistics it appears that in certain corrective institutions twenty per cent of the children suffer from endocrine complaints, and it is in this light that we must consider the delicate problem of human responsibility.'

According to Caridroit, the suppression of sexual hormones may sometimes have a good effect on the behaviour of criminals.[10] To which Alexis Carrel, who is the last person to be accused of excessive materialism, added courageously: 'The Christian virtues are more difficult to practice when the endocrine glands are deficient.' And what is true of hormones is equally true of all other biological 'conditions' no matter in which way they are caused.

No less certain are the effects on personal adjustment of psychological shocks and 'states', even though such effects cannot be detected chemically or microscopically. Poor reflexes, uncontrolled emotions, a guilt-ridden subconscious are just as real phenomena as endocrine secretions.

Thus as the great film of life unfolds before our mind's eye: the chance encounter of the parental chromosomes, the secret pre-natal life of the embryo and foetus, the drama of birth; the long period of infancy with all its lurking dangers, hereditary diseases and misfortunes; parental neglect, social adversity – indeed, all the adverse factors that stand in the way of the arduous task of the child's adaptation to adult life . . . we begin to feel the nagging doubt that the term *responsibility* may be devoid of all meaning.

I frankly confess that I cannot understand what Jean-Paul Sartre means when, in the name of his 'metaphysics of liberty', he maintains that man is what he is, not because of his physiological organization nor even because of his environment, but simply because he has 'constructed himself' by his own actions.

Personally, I obstinately cling to the opposite view, that man is what he is because he is born of a specific germ, and because that germ has been subjected to a host of external circumstances. Without wishing to act the part of the bumptious biologist who pronounces glibly on philosophical problems, I must insist that two beings born of identical germs and subjected to identical influences, must be identical not only physically but also psychologically, and must therefore behave in identical ways. If any philosophy were to grant me that and be logically consistent with that fact, I should gladly give it my earnest consideration. Until that happens, I must range myself – and without any pleasure, for I dislike sheltering behind any kind of 'ism' – in the camp of those who are called determinists. Though determinists are not concerned with questions of responsibility and merit they can, nevertheless, express moral judgements. As John Stuart Mill put it, the problem of moral distinctions is not the problem of the freedom of the will. Virtuous actions are loved and admired, and evil actions are decried, no matter if they are performed freely or otherwise.

The determinist judges moral conduct as the critic judges a work of art – by its effects. This does not mean that the determinist questions the usefulness of all social sanctions (which themselves constitute factors determining conduct). He knows that such sanctions may, by example, sway many from the path of delinquency who would otherwise have given in to temptation.

.   .   .   .   .

But enough of philosophy. . . . Far better to devote oneself to the prevention of maladjustment, than to vain speculation about human responsibility.

When we speak of prevention we refer largely to biological methods of avoiding, or ameliorating, the organic causes of maladjustment. As regards the genetic factors proper, i.e. the composition of the parental germ cells, there is little we can do at the moment, since the only effective means of modifying this heritage, and of eradicating harmful genes would involve coercive eugenic measures. Such measures run counter not only to our laws, but to public opinion also.

The care of the child must therefore begin with the care of the foetus: moral and physical hygiene on the mother's part, great care, avoidance of intoxicants, infections, emotional upsets, fatigue, and also of X-rays.[11]

Some authors have advised medical abortion where the mother has contracted German measles during the first two months of pregnancy (when, as we have seen, the foetus is particularly sensitive to the teratogenous effects of the rubella virus). Some have even suggested that all young girls be inoculated with the virus as a preventive measure, while others have thought that specified serotherapy might protect the foetus.

The battle against alcoholism is part of the battle against maladjustment. Quite apart from the direct effects of maternal alcoholism on the foetus, the social effects of paternal drunkenness can ruin a child's life just as easily. Here we touch upon a paramount problem of social hygiene, which could be solved fairly quickly, were it not for the inexcusable laxity of our politicians who, by their silence, have become the virtual accomplices of the poisoners of our country.

Advances in obstetric techniques ought to reduce appreciably the incidence of birth traumata which, as we have seen, are the direct causes of a number of mental or character deficiencies. According to Soviet obstetricians the practice of painless childbirth has reduced to 2 per cent the cases in which forceps are called for, and thus the incidence of meningeal haemorrhage in the newly born.

Once the child is born, all the resources of modern medicine must be used to prevent those organic troubles which give rise to maladjustment, or to cure them if they can no longer be prevented. Here anti-biotics, sulpha drugs, etc., hormone and chemical therapy (glutamic acid) and (exceptionally) shock therapy and neuro-surgery can play an increasing part.

Grafting, too, has been used in certain types of psychological aberration: May and Huignard, particularly, were successful in grafting a thyroid gland, taken from a foetus, on a young boy. In our species, grafts of embryonic organs are the only grafts which take; grafts of adult organs are not tolerated by other individuals. However, advances in this field may be expected, since Medawar and Snell's work holds out hope that the obstacle of organic specificity may be overcome.

Important advances can also be expected in psychobiology and particularly in psycho-chemistry. An entirely new type of chemistry is being constructed, and there is no reason why its findings should not be applied to our particular field. We could say quite generally that the etiology of maladjustment is such that there is hardly one medical or biological discovery that has no therapeutic applications to this problem. If I have ignored psycho-analysis in this connexion, it is only because its effects are only indirectly biological.

Before I conclude, just a word about the important social and human role that some maladjusted people can play. So far we have considered maladjustment as a mere short-coming, a handicap that is as much a burden for the bearer as it is for others. But there is a form of superior maladjust-ment in which certain inadequacies are balanced by exceptional gifts. Though these gifts may not spring directly from the maladjustment itself, there can be no doubt that they bear its marks. The names of Kafka and Van Gogh spring readily to mind. Needless to say, the fact that many geniuses were maladjusted does not mean that we ought to encourage the spread of maladjustment. All it means is that we must support genius *despite* these handicaps.

Heuyer tells us that many paranoiacs, who failed miser-ably at home and in school, were yet able to lead an acceptable and useful social life, thanks to creative gifts which they evinced even in their anguish and in their defiance. This merits a brief discussion of a common misunderstanding concerning the term maladjustment. Many have claimed that it would be wrong to try to adapt an individual to a society as imperfect as ours. All such endeavours could only serve to make man servile, thus preventing all hope of future social progress.

The only answer I can give is that adaptation is not just another term for conformity, or approval, and that when psychologists and psychiatrists speak of adaptation it is not the political or economic structure of society they have in mind.

Just because a man is adjusted to the basic needs of

social life – to social existence – because he has learnt to accept suffering and to submit to the discipline of work and of fellowship, because he has faced up to reality instead of escaping into myths or day-dreams every time he meets failure, deceit or frustration – in short, just because he has an honest, wise, and virile attitude to himself and to others, he need not necessarily be a party to hypocrisy and social injustice. Quite the contrary is the case, and his indignation, his refusal to submit and his revolt would be all the more effective for being adult rather than infantile, adjusted rather than neurotic.

.   .   .   .   .

Nor must we confound the kind of adaptation we have in mind with quite another type of adaptation. For the Darwinian, the best adapted members of a species are those best fitted to succeed over their fellows in the struggle for life.

If we apply this usage of the term to man, the best adapted people would often be the greatest cheats and liars, those who do not shrink from any means to get the better of their competitors, who, having the least scruples, have the greatest freedom of action. It goes without saying that when we wish our children to become adapted it is not this kind of adaptation we desire.

We hope, by adjusting them to life, to endow them with humane virtues, to give them dreams beyond profit and loss, to teach them to place ideals and duties before their own immediate interests, to help improve the society of which they are a part, so that hypocrisy, baseness and egoism will not be honoured and rewarded as they are today. In short, we hope to rear adjusted children so that, by improving society, they will give it a humane basis also.

'What childishness, what Utopian dreams,' I can hear my critics exclaim. 'Human nature is what it is, and as long as biology does not alter it, society will continue in much the same way. . . .' Now, one does not reach my age without having been touched by discouragement. The spectacle of modern civilization, seen from any point of view, does little to give us heart. It seems that some ironic destiny has decreed that any advance in one field must be balanced by regression in another; that the sum of human misery remain for ever constant.

Yet there is no need to despair as long as childhood, that great mystery of rebirth, continues to hold out its promise. Despair is wrong while we are yet uncertain of all the potentialities of youth, while we have not probed its every possibility. Between man's potential life and his real life lies as much hope as we dare ask for.

'The child is father of the Man,' Wordsworth exclaimed. If our children fail to fulfil their promise, if, as they grow older, we feel let down and cheated – have we ourselves a clear conscience and can we honestly say that we have never let our children down? Instead of holding ourselves up as examples to be imitated, instead of inflicting our own ignorance, errors and prejudices upon them, instead of thwarting and deceiving them at every turn, let us try to respect in our children what we ourselves may lack, for there, in any case, lies our only hope for the future.

REFERENCES

[1]*See* Jean Rostand: *L'Hérédité humaine*, P.U.F., 1952.

[2] *Introduction à la Psychiatrie infantile*, 1952.

[3] The father's age, too, may be an unfavourable factor since, if the father is old, his genes have had a greater chance of deteriorating under the effects of radio-activity.

[4] Toxoplasmosis, caused by a protozoon, the *Toxoplasma Gondii*, is responsible for lesions that may prove fatal to the infant.

[5] *Psychanalyse et Neurobiologie*, by J. de Ajuriaguerra, R. Diatkine and J. Garcia Badaraco, in La Psychanalyse d'aujourd'hui, vol. II, P.U.F., 1956.

[6] *La clinique psychanalytique. La Relation d'objet*, in La Psychanalyse d'aujourd'hui, P.U.F., 1956.

[7] Sub-classifications of the extrovert and introvert types.

[8] *De l'homme*, 1773.

[9] Lecture to the *Académie* in October 1947.

[10] *Psycho-physiologie des glandes endocrines*, P.U.F., 1946.

[11] It has been shown that X-rays are responsible for certain types of chorioretinitis.

5

Biological Unity and Diversity

THE problem of unity and diversity, does not arise in biology alone. To some extent, the march of differentiation, setting, as it does, diversity by the side of unity or, as Herbert Spencer put it, creating heterogeneity by the side of homogeneity, pervades all spheres of life. It can be found in society as in nature, in the life of the individual as in the life of his social group, in intellectual as in material life, in technical advances as in the evolution of ideas.

According to the philosopher Renouvier, unity and diversity are the two poles of all existence, and for Spencer the transition from unity to diversity was the fundamental law of all progress. Starting with biological ideas derived from German physiology, he maintained that the development of the earth, of society, of governments, of industry, of commerce, of language, of literature, of science and of art followed the same evolution from the simple to the complex that is characteristic of the development of all living beings and of the evolution of all species.

Examples: society began as a collection of individuals with the same rights and obligations; every man was originally warrior, hunter, fisherman and worker all at once. Then came specialization and with it social distinctions. We know to what extent the division of labour is a reality in our own society, and recall that the very term was originally borrowed by Adam Smith from biology. Durkheim wrote that 'not only are the tasks within a given factory highly specialized but each factory in turn is itself a specialized unit. . . . The division of labour is not restricted to the economic world, its growing influence can be observed in the most varied social spheres. Political, administrative and judicial functions are becoming more and more specialized. The same is true of artistic and scientific work also. We have gone a long way since the time when philosophy was the only science; it has split into a multitude of special disciplines, each with objects, methods and approaches of its own.'

Auguste Comte also complained about this fragmentation of science. What would he say today, when every discipline is whittled down and pulverized to the point where no man of science can pretend to grasp more than a small portion of even his own branch of knowledge? So rapid is this drive towards specialization, that its effects can be felt within the short span of one life.

To take a personal example, it is no longer possible, as it was in my youth, to claim knowledge of biology: we merely study some aspect of genetics, embryology, immunology, histology, ecology, or endocrinology. It is because of this increase in '-ologies' that team-work in research is becoming more and more essential.

Need we mention the proliferation of medicine into gastro-enterology, ophthalmology, radiology, otorhinolaryngology, neurology, phthisiology, urology, dermatology, etc.? Not to mention gerontology and podology! Or take the example of language which, originally nothing but a set of exclamations, evolved by coining distinct terms for each notion and for each shade of ideas or feelings.

This irresistible march from unity to diversity is not without drawbacks or even dangers. Economists have long deplored the sad consequences of the division of labour which, by leading to the performance of monotonous and restricted tasks, robs work of all its personal meaning. Marx accused mechanization of dismembering man and the reader will recall Jean-Baptiste Say's bitter reflections on the workman whose sole task it was to turn out the eighteenth part of a pin.

Carrel, for his part, strongly denounced the spiritual dangers arising from the departmentalization and fragmentation of knowledge. Deploring the fact that knowledge can no longer exist entire in any one brain, he expressed the hope that some men would devote their lives to gathering knowledge as such, thus safeguarding its unity and integrity. In the medical field, many specialists have ceased to look upon their patients as whole men, considering them instead as so many organs, if not parts of organs, with a consequent restriction of judgement that may border on fetishism. All illnesses are explained away as pituitary disorders or as related to the proportion of cholesterol in the blood.

Finally, as pedagogues have realized long ago, specialization may be a grave danger to education since only a wide cultural background can lay the intellectual foundations for fruitful inquiry. Some, it is true, have maintained that specialization in early life is a *sine qua non* of later skill and efficiency. Admittedly, as science and technology are becoming more and more specialized, it is perhaps unavoidable that the individual should follow suit, but is he to dissolve into a mere cog in the great machine, a mere cell in the great organism?

Now that we have stated the problem, let us examine its relevance to biology. To do so, we must shelve what doctrinal or sentimental preferences we may hold, the better to look at the positive facts. We shall begin by considering the transition from unity to differentiation in the development of the human being.

A human being is a colony of different types of cells, each type consisting of millions of individuals. Nerve cells, bone cells, blood cells, epithelial cells, gland cells, muscle cells, etc., are just so many characteristic and stable types differing in form, size, function, lifetime and behaviour.

Each cell consists of a nucleus and its surrounding protoplasm, called the cytoplasm. The nucleus contains the chromosomes consisting of genes which, in turn, seem to consist mainly of desoxyribonucleic acid (D.N.A.). D.N.A. has recently been the subject of a great deal of discussion in connexion with the directed mutation of ducks, and is currently thought to form the chemical basis of heredity.

All animals arise from a single cell, the ovum, which, in turn, is formed by the union of two germ cells: the maternal ovule and the paternal spermatozoon. The nucleus of the human ovum contains 48 chromosomes, 24 of which are derived from the father, and 24 from the mother. The development of the human being is the result of a sequence of cell divisions: the ovum dividing into two cells, then into four, eight, etc. As the cell divides, so do the chromosomes, so that, accidents excepted, every cell of the body receives the 48 chromosomes of the ovum.

Since the human ovum weighs less than a thousandth of a milligram, while the new-born baby weighs roughly seven pounds, cell divisions clearly involve cell growth. Nor is that the whole story. As we have seen, an organism is not a colony of *similar* cells. In other words, at some stage in the development, a process of *cellular differentiation* must have taken place. In Minot's opinion – an opinion to which we can fully subscribe – it is thanks to this process that each one of us has become what he is, and in particular has received his nerve cells and hence his mental faculties. And Minot added: 'If we fully understood the way in which this process of differentiation operates, we should not be far from understanding life itself.'

While I dare not claim that we have meanwhile come to understand the nature of cellular differentiation fully, it is true to say that we have learnt a great deal more since the day Minot wrote those words, mainly thanks to the remarkable work of the German biologist Hans Spemann who, in 1935, was awarded the Nobel Prize for Physiology and Medicine. Though Spemann worked largely on *Tritons*, small newts commonly found in pools and ponds and even in ditches, his results can be applied to other animals, man included.

The egg of the *Triton* is a small ovoid of brownish protoplasm surrounded by a transparent membrane. The female fertilizes the egg externally with a supply of semen previously supplied by the male during their graceful love-play. Some time later, this egg, like all fertilized eggs, begins to divide. In the course of roughly one day – the time depending on the temperature of the water – the egg has divided into a large number of cells; it now resembles a small mulberry, and is therefore called a morula (Latin *morum* = mulberry).

The morula acquires a central cavity and becomes the blastula, which, in turn, develops into the gastrula. Now, from his studies of the morula, the biologist – or rather the embryologist, for we must respect specialization! – knows by what processes this small multi-cellular sphere has become transformed into a full-grown vertebrate. He knows these processes in such detail that he can predict with certainty what part of the future animal will arise from what particular area or zone of the morula.

He knows – for so standardized and stereotyped is embryonic development – that the future epidermal cells will be formed in this spot and the future nerve cells in that (let us note in passing that the differentiation of the noto-chord marks the beginning of embryonic organization in general). Profiting from this knowledge, the embryolgist can carry out a most intriguing though very delicate experiment. (Nowadays, the experiment has become so common, that it is even being carried out under the scalpels of students.)

If, during the early stages of the embryo's life, a piece of presumptive epidermis is grafted into the neural plate region, it will behave like nervous tissue, while a piece of presumptive neural plate develops in epidermal regions into typical epidermis. In other words, the development of the embryo is in no way affected by the substitution. It follows its normal course: the skin cells becoming nerve cells, and the nerve cells becoming skin cells. At this stage, the cells are still identical; they are not yet differentiated – or if they are, at least not yet to the point where they can no longer change their destiny by changing position.

Thus, all the cells of the young embryo are interchange-able. They are said to be 'totipotent', i.e. they are jack-of-all-trade cells. We are still at the hour of unity, the hour of specialization has not yet struck. The future of a cell still depends on its position, its fate can be changed by simple displacement. Its potential future far exceeds its normal future.

.   .   .   .   .

Now let us repeat our experiment with another *Triton* egg, older by some hours (late gastrula stage). This time the result is quite different.

Epidermal cells remain epidermal cells and nerve cells remain nerve cells, no matter to what region they are transplanted. In other words, at this slightly later stage in the embryo's life, differentiation has begun to play an irrevocable and irreversible role. Distinctions between cells have become definite and can no longer be broken down by any manipulations. Their future is settled once and for all. No longer jack-of-all-trade cells, their potential future no longer exceeds their real future.

Spemann and his collaborators demonstrated yet another point of capital importance. Cell differentiation is not a simultaneous process but begins locally in an embryonic region called the primary organizer. If we transplant a piece taken from that region to another part of the same embryo, we shall find that the organs will no longer form in their normal position, but act as if they were under orders from the transplanted region.

Better still, if we transplant the piece to a different embryo, with an organizing centre of its own, we shall see that the graft will 'induce' a system of supernumerary organs forming a secondary embryo.

These experiments leave no doubt about the role of the primary organizers. It is in this privileged spot that cellular differentiation originates and then proceeds, each differentiated region leading to the differentiation of surrounding areas, by a kind of avalanche effect. It seems likely that cell differentiation is associated with the diffusion of chemical substances that are more or less comparable to hormones.

.   .   .   .   .

We could go a step further and ask how the primary organizers, the source of all differentiation, arose in the first place. While we do not know for certain, it seems likely that these special zones may result from the fact that the egg is not a perfectly homogeneous and isotropic cell. From this primary heterogeneity alone, certain embryonic cells may derive special faculties which they do not share with their sister cells.

This brings us to a very important point: though our somatic cells are the result of early cell differentiation, our reproductive cells, the so-called germ line, are not. Biologists have long been discussing whether this distinction between somatic and germ cells is, in fact, fundamental. Without taking sides in this specialist dispute, we are on safe ground in saying that everything happens *as if* this were so. In many animals, the separation of a special group of cells, the germ-line determinants, become apparent from the very beginning of the animal's development. Sometimes an 'island' of special protoplasm can be made out in even the undivided egg. If this little island is destroyed, the egg will produce animals totally devoid of germ cells. The excision is, in fact, an early form of castration, castration *ab ovo* as it were.

Contrary to earlier beliefs, germ cells are not distin-

[160]

guished from other cells by their potential immortality (which they are now known to share with many somatic cells), but only by their persistent lack of differentiation.

The egg, an undifferentiated cell, can therefore produce two types of cell, undifferentiated cells like itself which will form the germs, and differentiated cells which will form the body. Germ cells are never the result of the specialization of other cells – their lack of differentiation is continuous from one generation to the next. Non-differentiation may be considered a form of idle capital, put aside for the animal's future.

But to return to cell differentiation. Does it occur in the cell's nucleus, its cytoplasm, or in nucleus and cytoplasm together? There is a great deal of theoretical evidence that the nucleus is not basically involved. It can also be shown experimentally that D.N.A. (which is of course a nucleic acid) has apparently the same composition in all the cells of a given individual. But the crucial experimental evidence stems from the work of Briggs and King, two American biologists.

If the nucleus of the undeveloped egg of a frog is replaced with the nucleus of a cell from a frog embryo in which differentiation has already begun, the egg will develop normally, as if nothing had happened. At this stage of development all embryonic nuclei are not only equivalent to one another, but also to the nucleus of the egg. No *nuclear* differentiation has occurred. If the experiment is repeated with older embryonic cell nuclei, the results, though less clear and more difficult to interpret, do not seem to run counter to the general conclusion that differentiation occurs in the cytoplasm and not in the nucleus.

How does cytoplasmic differentiation come about?

According to some authors, the cytoplasm of different types of cells differs in the quality of its *plasmagenes*, special elements which resemble genes in that they, too, can reproduce their likeness, albeit outside the nucleus.

In any case, Etienne Wolff's work on culturing embryonic organs has shown that all tissues made up of the same type of cells (liver tissue, for example) even if they come from distant species, have a certain affinity for one another. Thus Wolff managed to create what he called 'absurd organs' by joining pieces of liver taken from ducks and mice and growing them together. It appeared that not only did the two pieces tolerate each other but that they arranged themselves together 'as if they recognized each other'. From this, Wolff inferred that they had a similar structure, i.e. that there exists a certain molecular kinship between the cytoplasm of cells of the same type, irrespective of the zoological distance between the species from which the cells are taken.

Let us now summarize what we have said about biological differentiation in the course of embryological development:

(1) Cellular differentiation does not appear until a certain stage of development is reached;

(2) Differentiation is directed from a certain embryonic area;

(3) A certain line of cells remains undifferentiated, this line will later give rise to the germ cells;

(4) Cellular differentiation seems to be principally or exclusively restricted to the cellular cytoplasm. All the cells of a given individual have something in common, and that something could be called the *cellular basis of individuality*.

As Le Dantec clearly realized, the cells in Paul's liver differ from the cells in his spleen, but, despite their differences, they also have a common factor that distinguishes them respectively from the cells in Joseph's liver and those in Joseph's spleen.

With this remark, we have returned to the quite distinct problem of the differentiation of individuals within a given species, one of the chief concerns of geneticists. This problem was discussed in Chapter IV and the conclusions can be summarized as follows:

(1) The innate (genetic) differences between individuals are due to the nucleus and not to the cytoplasm, and this fact distinguishes individual from cellular differentiation;

(2) Genetic differentiation is due partly to the mutation of genes, but mainly to sexual reproduction which, by the combination of a multitude of genes, leads to the creation of a host of individual types;

(3) This type of differentiation is characterized by the intolerance of the cells of one individual towards the cells of another. Moreover, this intolerance increases with age, two adults behaving as if they were even more incompatible than two youths and, *a fortiori*, than two embryos. All individuals develop from the completely undifferentiated stage to the most highly differentiated form. In the course of his embryonic development, man is a vertebrate before he becomes a mammal, a mammal before he becomes a primate, a primate before he becomes a hominid, a hominid before he becomes *homo sapiens*, a member of a species before he becomes a specific individual.

This is what von Baer meant when he said that, in the course of embryonic development, general traits appear before special traits, and common traits before specific traits. We might add that individual traits appear last of all.

.   .   .   .   .

Having examined both the differentiation of cells and also the differentiation of individuals within a given species, we shall now consider our last problem: the differentiation of species. For is not the species itself the result of differentiation within a given genus and the genus the result of differentiation within a given family?

According to the classical theory of evolution, a common stock may produce a number of branches which, in time, become more and more distinct from one another. This evolutionary differentiation – the mechanism of which is not known, though it is certainly connected with the inherited cell nucleus – almost invariably goes hand in hand with *specialization*, and an example will explain the meaning of that term.

There is no doubt that primitive mammals had a hand with five fingers, vaguely resembling that of our frog. Now this primitive hand must have given rise to the claws of the carnivore, to the hoof of the horse, to the flipper of the seal, the wing of the bat. All these 'hands' go with a certain mode of life and with certain habits, and are said to be specialized forms of the original and general type in which all subsequent forms must have been contained.

Here we have a process that strongly resembles the development and differentiation of the various types of cells.

In fact, the development of an individual has often been compared to the development of the entire animal kingdom and, even though the analogy may be a little superficial, it is not without value.

To some extent, specialization and differentiation represent a kind of evolutionary impasse, for nothing new can be born of an over-specialized type. Now, in the past, the major advances in life have been wrought by a succession of 'generalized' undifferentiated types and such types were called 'soft' or plastic by the philosopher Leroy, to emphasize the fact that they played the same part in the development of the species as the embryo plays in the development of the individual.

To revert to the example of the hand, man – the crown of evolution – has preserved the hand of the primitive mammal. This is a clear sign that, in the line from which man has sprung, specialization has never gone too far. In many other respects, too, man has retained marked traits of the primitive mammal. As Leroy put it, man has 'preserved with striking freshness certain zoological traits of the most ancient mammals known. His limbs, number of digits, and arrangement of teeth are strangely primitive.'

Not being specially adapted either to swimming, or to running, or to flying, not being good for any one thing man is good for everything. Compared with quaint animals like the giraffe, the bat, or the seal, man seems to be endowed with a pure, classical structure, so much so that we might call him *the* mammal, the king of mammals. It has been said of man that he is the only mammal that could be called an embryo.

Now, it is correct to assert that the future development of a species is always assured by completely or largely undifferentiated types, just as the parental future of the individual is assured by the germinal tissue which is devoid of all specialization. Moreover, and we do not wish to labour the point, according to the theory of neoteny or pedomorphosis, all great evolutionary changes and innovations have been wrought by some kind of return to the embryonic type or, more generally, to the juvenile type.[1]

According to this theory, a line that has apparently become sterile and senile because of over-specialization, may assume the characteristics of the embryo, i.e. less specialized and less differentiated traits, and thus become rejuvenated. This is said to apply to man, that descendant of the ape, who, it is pointed out resembles the foetus of the ape much more than he does the full-grown animal.

.   .   .   .   .

But let us leave hypotheses that are only hypotheses, and return to the known facts. We have seen that the transition from the homogeneous to the heterogeneous occurs not only in the development of the individual, but also in that of the species, and finally of the animal kingdom.

Do these biological facts apply equally well to other fields such as, for instance, psychology and sociology? I must confess that, on principle, I am suspicious of all generalizations of that kind. We have seen that, even within biology, the processes of differentiation are dissimilar, and we are all aware what dangers are inherent in any comparisons between biological and other phenomena. Nevertheless, some conclusions may be drawn legitimately.

In the embryo just as in the species, all progress involves gradual differentiation. In this respect biology is in agreement with current opinions about the division of labour and the evolution of societies and technology. But over and above this, biology has something else to teach us, something that is perhaps quite new: the role of non-differentiation which is not something inferior, or a handicap but, on the contrary, a *positive factor*.

We have seen that it is the absence of differentiation in germ cells, which leads to the reproduction of individuals. Though non-differentiation is not a state of immortality, as Weismann believed, it is, nevertheless, a condition of toti-potence. Only because the egg is an undifferentiated cell, can it reproduce a complete animal, unlike, say, a hepatic cell which can never produce any but hepatic cells, a cartilage cell which can only produce cartilage cells, or a blood cell which gives rise to none but blood cells. Similarly, in the evolution of species, a highly specialized form is a final and fixed form of which little or nothing further can be expected. It is the undifferentiated forms that contain all future potentialities. We could say that, by and large, actual *progress depends on differentiation, while potential progress is possible only by virtue of non-differentiation.*

Non-differentiation is a kind of insurance against exhaustion, senility and mechanization; it is like a reservoir of freshness, full of promise for the future.

Leroy thought that, in this respect, the phenomena of life could be compared to those of thought. He remarked on the similarity between non-differentiation and invention, on the one hand, and between differentiation and automatism on the other: 'Institutions, societies, codes of behaviour or philosophic systems always follow the same evolutionary rhythm: water-tight explanations that are the triumphs of one epoch, reveal their impotence when confronted with the thoughts of another; the hardening of habits provokes

[167]

a lethal form of ankylosis, and while the promise of the future belongs to the inventive mind, hypertrophy extinguishes the virtues of initiative, and causes our institutions to be swamped by scholasticism.' And since philosophy was a less rigidly circumscribed discipline than science, and hence a less differentiated form of thinking, Leroy looked upon philosophy as the handmaiden of future progress and spiritual renewal.

I quite agree that the role of non-differentiation, the part played by the primitive and the youthful in biological processes, must be taken into consideration by any student of the evolution of societies, techniques, arts and ideas. I still remember my brief polemic on this subject with the philosopher Julien Benda who, stout thinker though he is, dislikes any form of criticism or contradiction.

He had just published an attack on the primitive and infantile – non-differentiated, as we might say – tendencies of modern writers,[2] in which he believed to see clear evidence of spiritual deterioration and decadence. In the name of biology, I took the liberty of reminding him that as far as living beings were concerned, infantile, primitive and undifferentiated processes often represented progress, actual or potential. This simple reminder made our philosopher see so red, that he accused me of intellectual barbarism and demagogy.

Julien Benda notwithstanding, should individuals, groups, schools of thought or philosophy, and political parties be encouraged to cater for non-differentiation, plasticity and immaturity?

This conclusion might be a little too narrow, too rigid, too differentiated. . . . And, moreover, it is by no means certain that, while profiting by differentiation, we can deliberately cultivate non-differentiation by its side. Only nature may have her cake and eat it. . . .

What does seem certain is that individuals, groups, or schools of thought, will not evolve or advance, change or adapt themselves unless they contain undifferentiated elements, the buds of all future growth, and unless they retain the secret of youth in heart and mind.

'*La beauté de l'enfance est de ne pas finir.*'

REFERENCES

[1] Cf. G. N. de Beer: *Embryology and Evolution.*
[2] *La France byzantine.*

6

Biology and the Cinema

I SHOULD like to make it perfectly clear right from the start that I am no expert on films. I have not been to a cinema for more than twenty years, nor have I ever had occasion to use scientific films in my own work. True, I have collaborated with Nicole Vedrès and André Labarthe in such films as *La Vie Commence Demain* and *Aux Frontières de l'Homme*, but only in the capacity of scientific adviser – my contribution being confined to editing, commentating and suggesting suitable pictorial material.

However, the role of the cinema in biology is so far-reaching and impinges on so many fields, particularly on the spreading of scientific, and perhaps of philosophic, knowledge, that even the non-specialist may be permitted to offer some pertinent, if general, comments.

To begin with, it must be obvious that the artificial eye of the camera has a great many advantages over the organic, human, eye. It is, for instance, indefatigable. While the human eye cannot follow continuous processes for even an hour, the camera can do so for days, if not for weeks or months, and without the slightest lack of attention. Moreover, while the camera is impersonal, impartial and perfectly objective, the eye cannot help being influenced by the beholder's conscious or unconscious attitudes, his prejudices, his afterthoughts, his desires and his hopes. *Quod enim mavult homo verum esse, it potius credit*, Bacon said – man sees only what he wants or expects to see. Adding or suppressing, he rejects or alters reality to suit his needs.

Again, even could the human eye be perfectly impartial,

it has only a restricted field of vision. Thus it may not be able to take in an entire phenomenon and may have to disperse and divide its attention by darting from place to place. Each act of concentration on a given point simply means lack of attention to other points. The camera, on the other hand, can capture an entire process on a film which can subsequently be analysed and scrutinized at leisure – just like a butterfly collection.

Furthermore, thanks to the cinema – the 'machine for printing life', as Marcel Lherbier called it – we become the masters of events, inasmuch as we can force them to run their course all over again, at will, thus resuscitating the past in all its original freshness. Just as a ruthless film-director can whip his actors to respond to his every whim, so can we order the sun to spit out its flames, the volcano to throw up its lava, the leucocyte to pounce upon the microbe, the paramecium to divide itself, the chromosome to execute its strange ballet, the male hippocampus to writhe in 'labour pains'. . . .

Or else, events for ever at our finger-tips and ever-ready to be reborn under our eyes, can be stopped and frozen into immobility whenever we so desire it. We can petrify the privileged moment, so that nothing may escape our scrutiny. The gentlest quiver of a speck of protoplasm, the least hesitation of a flagellum, the slightest flicker of a cilium can be caught and detected. No phenomenon, however transitory, can escape our scrutiny, the moment its imprint has been recorded on celluloid.

By mere sleight of hand we can even alter the rhythm of events. We can detect movement where we might have suspected immobility, and, conversely, observe motions that are normally too quick to be followed. Claude Mauriac said that the cinema captures time without immobilizing it, imposing a new rhythm on cadences of nature that were previously hidden from our gaze.

In addition to all these advantages, the photographic emulsion reacts to infra-red and ultra-violet rays to which our retinas, and for that matter the retinas of most animals, are insensitive. By filming phenomena in the light of these invisible rays, the naturalist can take visible pictures in 'biological darkness', the better to study the behaviour of camera-shy animals.

Last but not least, the camera makes it possible to preserve for all time exceptional and unique events. If we add that all these advantages over the human eye apply to all distances and to all magnitudes, the reader will appreciate that the cine-camera has endowed man with a veritable new sense organ. By improving man's visual apparatus and by widening his powers of perception, the cinema has played the part of an organic and structural extension to our visual capacities.

In a recently published book,[1] the great Jesuit palaeontologist Teilhard de Chardin writes that 'the history of living nature might well be called the elaboration of ever more perfect eyes within an ever-widening world of observable events. Do we not judge an animal's place in the scale of things, and the supremacy of man as the thinking being, by the penetration and synthetic power of their gaze? Our attempts to see more and better are thus neither fantasies, idle curiosity nor luxury. We must see or perish.'

And from the same book I also quote the following passage which seems to apply with particular force to motion pictures: 'We must seek out the irresistible changes that are latent in very slow processes, where extreme agitation hides under the disguise of rest, and originality is embedded in the heart of monotonous repetition.'

.   .   .   .   .

Perhaps it is permissible to consider the acquisition of this new eye, this new instrument of vision, as the beginning of a new stage in man's biological evolution, which is, in fact, continued by all advances in technology. Improvements of visual power are by no means the only examples of the extension of natural by human invention – of phylogenesis by technogenesis. Man's ability to count and to reason has been improved by electronic computers, his means of locomotion by motor-cars and aeroplanes, and his reproductive powers by artificial insemination.

'In our search for the real roots of technology, we must look at palaentology – biology in the larger sense,' Leroi-Gourain wrote. And the Serbian physiologist Jean Giaja, in a recent essay on 'Man and the Inventive Life', stressed the fact that inventive prowess is the origin of civilization and of the living world. Without dwelling on such grave philosophic problems, let us now examine some applications of the cinema to scientific research.

One way in which the camera has particularly shown its worth is in the study of the solar prominences, those immense jets of gas that are thrown up from the solar surface. Some of these jets shoot out into space with fantastic speeds, to reach heights of well over five hundred thousand miles. Now the French astonomer Bernard Lyot, by using extreme high-speed photography, managed to demonstrate the actual movements of the luminous mass, and its return to the solar chromosphere after its vast journey through space.

The cinema has also been of great help in the study of volcanic eruptions, or aurorae, of eclipses, of the melting of glaciers, of such physical phenomena as Brownian movement, surface tension, the movements and propagation of flames and the propagation of sound waves. Still, the reader will forgive us if we concentrate on the role of the cinema in biology.

Here its chosen field is the study of animal movements and, by and large, the films are taken at high speed and then shown in slow motion, since the movements are generally too fast to be observed and interpreted directly.

'The cinema,' Magnan said, 'is the most powerful means of investigating and analysing movement.'

It will be remembered that it was through the study of animal movements that the cinema was originally born. In 1878, Eadweard Maybridge, an English photographer and a student of animal locomotion working in the United States, was asked to settle a bet between two millionaires as to whether a trotting horse lifts all four feet from the ground at the same time, or not. In order to do so, Maybridge took a number of photographs of the moving animal at close intervals. As a reward, Leland Stanford, Governor of California and the winner of the bet, gave him a grant to study the movements of other animals also.

A little later, in 1882, Marey used his chronophotograph to study the flight of gulls and the gait of man. Ten years later he produced the first motion picture consisting of sixty separate frames. Then came Edison in 1889 and, above all, the brothers Lumière in 1895, and it is to them that we owe those crucial improvements which turned the cinema

[177]

into the great instrument of exploration, instruction and entertainment that it has become today.

In the study of animal movements, speed is of the utmost importance. Thus to analyse the flight of insects with their rapid wing-beat – 250 beats per second in the bee – 25,000 photographs per second must be taken if each wing-beat is to be broken down into its phases. In the case of other, slower, movements twenty pictures per second may suffice.

Ultra-rapid cameras provide up to 1,000,000 pictures per second, and Professor Bull thinks that this can be increased to up to 3,000,000 pictures per second. If he is right an entirely new world would open up to us.

But even without such powerful aids, Magnan was able to use his very beautiful film of the flight of insects, to analyse each wing-beat, to study stationary flight, gliding, aerial manœuvres, and, finally, to put forward a theory on the mechanics of insect flight.

It appears that of all insects diptera (flies) and hymenoptera (bees) have the greatest number of wing-beats per second (bee = 250; fly = 160); butterflies are much slower (8–50 beats per second) and so is the cockchafer (46), the rose chafer (86) and the dragon-fly (20–40).

The movement of other animals has also been studied on film: the frog's leap, the millepede's crawl – a very strange phenomenon indeed, since the feet are uncoordinated – the sea-horse's propulsion, the creep of the starfish, the flight of the humming-bird and the walk of the chimpanzee, the movement of lip and vocal cords during human speech, man's pupillary and pharyngeal reflexes, heart-beats and peristaltic movements.

Similarly, films have been used to study the behaviour of

plants (particularly of carnivorous plants), and to observe the movement of uni-cellular organisms, such as infusoria, bacteria, spermatozoa, pigment cells, etc.

By taking high-speed films, Dr. Comandon was able to produce remarkably clear pictures of the movement of white blood corpuscles (leucocytes) as, according to Albert Delaunay, 'they throw themselves upon microbes as a flock of gulls would upon aquatic prey'. Dr. Comandon does, in fact, deserve special mention. As early as 1909 he managed to produce biological and microbiological films that were classic masterpieces and have remained models to this day. No one can look at his films without marvelling at their unsurpassed quality, which stands comparison with even the best of modern films.

His, and other films, have played an important role in our study of the behaviour and life of cells. The division of chromosomes, nuclear grafts in the amoeba, the growth of normal and malignant cells *in vitro*, the elongation and differentiation of nerve fibres, the reaction of cells to chemical agents, to radiation, to supersonic waves and to electric currents, the destruction of bacteria by lytic viruses or bacteriophages, are just a few of the principal subjects investigated. Here we must draw attention to only one major discovery due to the camera: the observation of protoplasmic currents, too slow to be seen with the naked eye, and only demonstrable by the technique of photographing the phenomenon at spaced out intervals. By emphasizing as never before the close connexion between life and movement, pictures of this intercellular dynamic process, of this ceaseless vital turbulence, have affected our very approach to the problem of life.

We cannot dwell on a great many other remarkable

achievements of the cinema such as filming the meta-
morphosis of flies, the spinning of cobwebs, the love-play
and combat of certain fishes, or even the scattering of scent
by the rose as it bombards us with talcum particles. All we
have time to discuss is von Frisch's remarkable work on the
language of bees, one of the most astonishing discoveries
ever made in the field of animal psychology.

When a honey-gathering bee comes upon a rich find of
nectar-producing flowers, she returns to the hive to share
her discovery with her fellow-workers. They quickly form
closed ranks and make straight for the floral provender.
It is due to von Frisch, the famous Austrian scientist, that
we know how this is done.

The foraging bee describes a figure 8 inside the hive,
her speed indicating the distance from the flowers, and the
inclination of the figure to the horizontal platform the
direction to be followed. This 'dance-language' is, of
course, inborn. In that respect, the bee is superior to the
human being and this despite the fact that its brain weighs
less than a tenth of a milligram. Not even Fabre, who was
often accused of exaggerating the importance of the
instinct of insects, ever dreamt of anything like this, nor did
Maeterlinck, the great romanticizer of the bee. Once again
truth has proved stranger than fiction.

In 1926, von Frisch – that 'Champollion of the bees'[2]
as Maurice Mathis called him – took a film of this marvellous dance, and, by running the film at slow motion, he was
able to analyse the bee's complicated manœuvres in the
hive. His films were shown at a number of scientific con-
gresses, so that biologists and psychologists from every
part of the world could share his new-found knowledge,
and see the dancing language with their own eyes. Before

he showed the film, von Frisch had been the butt of a great many ironical gibes. Here the cinema was able to play a considerable role in swinging his opponents round, a role that is quite distinct from pure research. In other instances also, the cinema has greatly reduced the time it takes for a new truth to be accepted. By enabling a discoverer to judge the value of his work step by step, and to share his observations and discoveries with others, the cinema has become an unrivalled means of scientific communication.

.　　　.　　　.　　　.　　　.

Animal psychology also owes a great debt to the cinema. The great Austrian scientist K. Lorenz used films to study how bird behaviour is affected, particularly by the first visual images received on being hatched, and the Kellogs filmed the mental development of a baby chimpanzee which they brought up as a member of the family.

In the field of human psychology, Prudhommeaux filmed the main stages of the psycho-motor development of a child from birth till the age of three; he followed the gradual progress made in the child's powers of prehension, in the co-ordination of gestures, and in play.

Gesell, who observed children with the same care, the same patience and the same vigilance that von Frisch had bestowed on his bees, took films of even the slightest responses of the child's pupils and lips, of its first attempts at grasping and walking and of increases in its power of attention. Comparing the psychological development of various children, and particularly of twins, he endeavoured to determine what individual factors went into their making. Gesell was emphatic that films alone enabled him to carry out a careful and continuous analysis, since, by their coherency, their unquestionable authenticity and their 'quantifiability', they illustrated infantile responses in the best possible way.

Finally – if in a somewhat different sphere – we must mention Spitz's important films on the development of cognition in the infant (the growth of feelings, the beginning of interest in others, the first smile, etc.). In particular, he investigated the emotional ties between mother and child. Previously, the full effects of these ties had not been appreciated sufficiently, and no one could have asserted that an individual's entire future can be shaped for good or bad by the mother's early influence.

Spitz was able to show that the child derives his feelings of security from his mother – or his mother substitute. If a child is deprived of maternal love – or at least of a modicum of maternal love – serious troubles in the form of emotional blockages (affect blocks) may result. The longer the situation persists the graver the consequences.

Spitz's remarkable films compare the behaviour of children reared at home with that of children brought up in day-nurseries, crèches, etc. Though the material conditions, distractions and toys may be the same in both cases, there is one striking difference: in one case the child has the mother all to itself, while in the other it only has a portion of her.

The poet spoke truly when he said of maternal love that 'though shared by all, each has his fullest part'. Children who do not have their full portion of maternal love become restless, anxious, and inhibited. The result is withdrawal, lack of vitality, hebetude, insomnia, fits of temper and jealousy, and progressive mental deterioration. All this can be read from the children's expressions, gestures, attitudes and inflections on Dr. Spitz's twenty thousand yards of film.

What strikes the layman even more forcibly is that these partial 'orphans' – 'orphans' despite the care with which they are treated – show signs of physical deterioration: stunted growth, loss of appetite and weight, malnutrition, increased susceptibility to disease – the slightest cut leading to an infection, the slightest illness taking serious forms. No wonder that the mortality rate is far greater in children brought up in nurseries than in children reared at home.

Other films – e.g. *Monique*, a film by Jenny Aubry, etc. – have much the same story to tell.

. . . . .

Another important role of the cinema is to preserve – if only on film – animals on the point of extinction.

Unfortunately, some animals about to be destroyed by mankind, have become the fossils of tomorrow. Thus, the gorilla, the giraffe, the okapi, the kiwi have almost left the terrestrial scene, just as the *Aepyornis* (a genus of gigantic fossil bird that still lived in the nineteenth century, since we know that Auguste Geoffrey Saint-Hilaire received a present of its eggs), and the *Didus ineptus* or Dodo of Mauritius (a bird about as large as a swan with a very stout hooked bill that still existed at the end of the seventeenth century) have already become extinct almost within living memory.

Claude Mauriac was quite right to claim that 'before the invention of the cinema, no explorer or scientist had even one thousandth part the natural knowledge that the most sedentary and ignorant of men can acquire nowadays. The cinema makes us privy to the most secret spectacles of nature, revealing the secrets of life from the infinitely great to the infinitesimally small. We are brought close to the stars, we descend into the ocean's depths . . . we observe all the intimate forms of life in their thousands of facets.'

In teaching – from the elementary school to the university – the cinema daily plays a more considerable role. According to Henri Laugier, 'the generations formed by books are separated by a gulf from those formed by the cinema'.

Clearly, the attention of the young child, who is first and foremost an animistic spectator, can be much more surely held by the picture than by the word.

The cinema also has a special role to play in medicine and surgery. Films on vivisection obviate a great deal of repeated animal suffering, and surgical films, enable students to be 'present' at a masterful operation and to observe in its every least detail, with the added advantage that the operation can be stopped and repeated at will.

Moreover, the film immortalizes the skill of the great surgical virtuosos, just as gramophone records immortalize a great singer. Even the surgeon himself can benefit from films of his own work: by scrutinizing his operations, he can rectify or improve certain gestures. Such films are of historical interest, and not to him alone.

This brings us to yet another aspect of the cinema. Who would not be moved today to see the Curies working in their shed as they managed to isolate radium, to see Claude Bernard dissecting rabbits in his damp cellar, to watch Pasteur supervising the first inoculation with anti-rabies vaccine, or to behold the great Fabre working in *La Harmas*, his retreat in Serignan?

No doubt, Pierre Fresnay plays the part of *Monsieur Fabre* admirably well, but how much should we not prefer to see the grand old man himself, even if he played his own role only half so well!

To be just, I should also have to mention the film's important role in spreading social hygiene, in improving the means of medical diagnosis, etc. But I shall merely draw attention to one of the cinema's least-known aspects – its philosophical role. I am not so much thinking of films that have tried to give an ingenious explanation of the fourth dimension or of relativity theory, but of purely biological films such as those taken by Dr. Comandon.

In 1952, the famous physiologist, Louis Lapique – who made an appreciable contribution to our understanding of the nervous system – presented two very strange papers to the *Institut*, in which he put forward the hypothesis that each cell is a self-contained organism, an 'individual' as it were, and that cellular life has psychological as well as material aspects. Man's consciousness, according to Lapique, is some sort of resultant of all his many 'cellular souls'.

Now, Lapique claimed that his hypothesis is, in fact, strongly borne out by observations of the behaviour, on film, of such cells as, for instance, white blood corpuscles. Referring to Dr. Comandon's famous film, mentioned earlier, Lapique said: 'Whenever I have projected that film the audience has always shown signs of being deeply impressed by the spectacle of these tempestuous monsters colliding with, and throwing themselves upon, the red corpuscles, the better to forge their passage in a chosen direction.'

For Lapique, the positivist physiologist, the soul of the

leucocyte was non-material but not immortal. Similarly, for Haeckel, who was also a firm believer in cellular consciousness: 'Every naturalist who, like myself, has observed the psychological activity of unicellular organisms over many years, is positively convinced that they, too, are possessed of consciousness. This cellular soul like any other, is made up of a number of sensations, ideas, and volitional acts. The sensations, the thought and the will of our own psyche are nothing but the gradual developments of that consciousness. . . . Like the new psychology and pathology, the psychology and psychiatry of the future must become cellular, and concentrate on the psychological function of cells.'[3]

But the hypothesis of the cellular 'soul' or consciousness need not be tied to a materialist philosophy, and is also held by a great many idealists. Conversely, some idealist biologists, such as L. Bounure, reject the hypothesis as unfounded.[4]

Now, irrespective of which of the contending philosophic parties is correct, it is obvious that, since one of them adduces the film as an argument in favour of its point of view, the cinema has begun to play an important part in even this branch of knowledge. The cinema would seem to support Cournot's contention that 'all the difficulties and mysteries with which philosophers have been concerned, particularly [the mystery] of the phenomenon of human consciousness, spring from the very grounds of life'.

Films of cellular phenomena do, in fact, suggest a highly anti-Cartesian view of life. As we watch these viscous globules feeding, dividing and moving in a given direction, we truly gain the impression – I must insist on the word 'impression' since the argument provided by the cinema can never be more than intuitive – that we are confronting anything but a machine, however complex, such, for instance, as cyberneticists are busily constructing by means of electronic 'hardware'. It seems that the difference is emphasized even more strongly when we observe the behaviour of a microscopic infusorium than when we look at a higher animal. Paradoxical though it may sound, the simple cell strikes us as far more inimitable than the finished animal with its tubes, vessels, fibres, nerve impulses – all its mechanics, hydraulics and pneumatics. While Grey Walter's tortoises with their 'reflexes', adaptive 'behaviour', and 'memory', and also 'thinking' machines which imitate and even surpass our powers of logical reasoning, may well remind us of familiar creatures, we feel certain that no machine can ever imitate the quivering of protoplasm, the vibration of a cilium, or the pulsation of a vesicle. . . .[5]

.   .   .   .   .

It must be emphasized that the value of biological films goes much further than mere instruction. When, on the screen, we see infusoria swarming in a drop of water, or white blood corpuscles throwing themselves upon bacteria, we seem to be in direct contact with cellular life. The impression is more than merely visual; we seem to touch and to feel the presence of these living creatures, we are tickled by their cilia. . . .

We sense the exuberance, the ubiquity of the mystery of life. In face of the complexities of the magnified cell, we understand how Pascal could become so excited about a mere mite, that he could call it 'an universe unto itself'. . . .

As we look at a drop of blood swarming with corpuscles, we are forcibly reminded of Goethe's dictum that each man is a crowd. Indeed, we are no longer spectators but actors as well. We become the companions, the kinsmen of these minute creatures. The film takes us on a strange voyage – one of those fantastic excursions into the world of small dimension that has inspired so many writers from Swift and Voltaire to Maurice Renard. Satisfying what Prof. Schuhl has called 'the Gulliver complex', the film, by changing our scale of dimensions, transplants us into other worlds.

Just as the film drives home the relativity of magnitudes, so it forcibly reminds us of the relativity of time, of how strongly our ideas depend on the personal rhythm of our sensations.

Sainte-Lagüe invented a fictional character, *Lentus* by name, whose sensations were so slow that, to him, a tenth of a second was like a day, and the snail progressed with meteoric speed. *Lentus* was contrasted with *Rapidus*, a being whose sensations were so quick that even the fastest events seemed almost immobile and fixed. By projecting films at slow and rapid motion, the cinema can now turn each of us into a Lentus or Rapidus, at will. . . .

As we see a plant complete its full life cycle within a few minutes – germination, sprouting, flowering and foliation – we ourselves are speeded up, and conversely when we are present at the slow bursting of a soap bubble or watch the even beat of the dragon-fly's wing we ourselves are slowed down.

From philosophy it is but a short step to aesthetics and it cannot be denied that beauty is radiated by some, if not by all, nature films. We have only to mention Jean Painlevé's wonderful pictures of such aquatic assassins as the octopus, the sea-urchin, daphnia, the hippocampus, or the vampire. Films of that quality demand years of hard work and much patience – to produce a spectacle lasting but a few minutes.

Financially, however, the whole thing, one might say, is a dead 'loss'. Moreover, the mere mention of documentary films 'sets cinema managers scampering as if they had heard a leper's cry' (Raymond Millet). Thus, for the moment at least, it seems unlikely that the cinema will produce great biological epics on, for instance, the development of man, heredity, the evolution of the animal kingdom or the future of our species. Even so, thanks to the work of Painlevé, Comandon, Dragesco,[6] and others, we can already share their joy in the prodigious beauty of life, and the spectacle is further enhanced by the fact that it was not captured for gain or personal glory.

All nature seems captivating, the moment it is magnified, and projected on the screen. No matter to what level we descend, we cannot help marvelling at the wonderful sights unfolding before us. The eyes of the louse, the egg of the grasshopper, a thread from the spider's spinneret, the birth of a fly, the swaying of a leaf, the vibration of the toad's throat – each is breath-taking in its own way.

True enough, all that beauty is only in the eye of the beholder. But does it not make us marvel all the more at the miraculous way in which our eye can derive so much beauty from nature's treasure-house of spectacles?

.　.　.　.　.

We have just extolled the scientific film, and the great many parts it plays in our life. We have seen what service it can render to science, to our search for truth, to its demonstration and spread, to immortalizing exceptional or unique phenomena, to the philosophic interpretation of life, and finally to our direct and sensory contact with living reality. Have we, then, no reservations at all about the use and distribution of scientific films?

Some have held that the cinema produces some kind of 'visual indigestion' which, in the long run, can turn man away from reality – the picture, as it were, taking the place of real experience. Others again have held that civilization is increasingly threatened by ignorance of the spoken or written word. The power of abstraction, they claim, is in danger of atrophying as less and less heed is given to the writings of the great.

People have even gone so far as to accuse the cinema of cheapening serious instruction by making it too easy and attractive. . . . Possibly there is some grain of truth in all these objections. A beautiful wife is always a danger to one's peace of mind, and there is no progress without some setbacks. Civilization has had the effect of tempering the brute strength of our savage ancestors, and Andre Lwoff has shown that all organic evolution involves 'losses of function' at every stage. But looking at the whole subject in perspective, I believe I am right in saying that, all in all, the damage caused by the scientific film is negligible when compared with its advantages.

As for the entertainment film, I must repeat that I know next to nothing about it. I have often heard it said that it is not exactly the instrument of intellectual and moral enlightenment that it could be, and I know perfectly well that Alexis Carrel blamed the film – together with the radio and the sweeping generalizations of school broadcasts – for contributing to that 'crisis of the spirit' which caused him so much anguish. . . . But is it the film that must be blamed, rather than those social and moral conditions which force its producers to satisfy the public's basest whims? Technical progress can never reward the soul with more than it deserves.

For my part, I am convinced that one single film by Jean Painlevé, by von Frisch, or by Dr. Comandon, clears the mind of a great many cobwebs. If, perchance, the reader should feel inclined to betake himself to the cinema, let us hope that he will come out with a better understanding of the eruptions of the sun, of the life of the cell, of the language of bees, and of the blessings of maternal love.

REFERENCES

[1] *Le Phénomène Humain*, 1954. (The Phenomenon of Man, London, 1959.)

[2] Jean François Champollion deciphered the Egyptian hieroglyphics in 1822.

[3] *Monism*, Schleicher, p. 34.

[4] *Revue scientifique*, 1950.

[5] The protozoon is nearer to human consciousness than even the most perfect machine which is never anything but an apparatus produced by man. . . . Consciousness is tied to true sensibility; it is an attribute of life.' (P. Chauchard: *Les machines à calculer et la Pensée humaine*, 1953.)

[6] Famed for his gripping films on termites, African butterflies etc.

INDEX